THE UNIVERSITY OF TENNESSEE LIBRARIES

*Occasional Publication*

NUMBER 1 • SPRING 1970

The *Occasional Publication* of The University of Tennessee Libraries is intended to be very flexible in its content and in its frequency of publication. As a medium for descriptive works related to various facets of library collections as well as for contributions of merit on a variety of topics, it will not be limited in format or subject matter, nor will it be issued at prescribed intervals·

JOHN DOBSON, EDITOR

JOHN C. HODGES
1892–1967

THE JOHN C. HODGES COLLECTION OF

# William Congreve

In The University of Tennessee Library:
A Bibliographical Catalog.

*Compiled by*
ALBERT M. LYLES and JOHN DOBSON

KNOXVILLE · THE UNIVERSITY OF TENNESSEE LIBRARIES · 1970

Library of Congress Catalog Card Number
73-631247

# INTRODUCTION

In a poignant note found among his class outlines for one of his last seminars in Restoration and eighteenth-century English literature, John C. Hodges, Professor of English at The University of Tennessee from 1921 to 1962 and head of the English Department from 1937 to 1962, had written, "Forty years with Congreve—and only 2 slender volumes, and some dozen articles to show." Although a modest man, even he must have recognized that his note did not reflect his achievement in his biography, *William Congreve the Man*, and his discovery and publication of Congreve's book list, *The Library of William Congreve*. Following his retirement from teaching, John Hodges climaxed a scholarly life devoted almost exclusively to Congreve with his edition of Congreve's letters. Another result of that devotion was his Congreve library, which contains more than one hundred pre-1800 editions of the dramatist's plays, poems, and collected works. That collection he left to The University of Tennessee Library at his death on July 7, 1967.

John Hodges did not amass his collection simply for his private use. Even before his death its users ranged from graduate students working on Ph.D. dissertations to his close friend Herbert Davis, who collated the Hodges quartos in preparing his edition of Congreve's plays. With the belief that John Hodges would wish his collection to be of the widest use to the scholarly world and with the desire to acknowledge his generous gift, we have compiled this bibliographical catalog.

In undertaking our catalog, we discovered that bibliographical research on Congreve has not been extensive. The Ashley and Pforzheimer catalogs have some fully described entries, and Woodward and McManaway, Hugh Macdonald, Donald Wing, and Carl Stratman provide some limited information. However, the only comprehensive listing, compiled by John P. Anderson as a supplement to Gosse's biography of Congreve, is quite inadequate. It is for this reason that, although we are describing only single copies, we have been as detailed as possible in our description of the items in the Hodges collection. Yet even with our limited perspective and aim we have discovered four eighteenth-century editions of *The Mourning Bride* not listed by Carl Stratman in his *Bibliography of English Printed Tragedy 1565–1900* (see items 60., 63., 68., and 73.); and we are publishing, we believe for the first time in a bibliographical work, descriptions of some of the ornaments used by Jacob Tonson and his heirs, one of the most important of late Restoration and early eighteenth-century publishing firms.

A definitive bibliography of Congreve—like Hugh Macdonald's *Dryden* but more detailed—is still needed not only for its obvious bibliographical value but also as an essential tool to be used with the monumental *The London Stage 1660–1800* and Emmett Avery's *Congreve's Plays on the Eighteenth-Century Stage* in the assessment of Congreve's reputation prior to 1800. Even from our study we have been aware that *Love for Love* and *The Mourning Bride* were published more frequently than the other three plays. And such a bibliography would make possible sounder texts of Congreve's plays than are now available—even in Herbert Davis's edition. It is now known that the plays were modified in a number of subsequent editions—not simply in the 1710 collected edition—as, for example, Fredson Bowers has noted for *The Mourning Bride*. A definitive bibliography would provide editors with a means for studying the history of these changes.

In the present work our aim has been to provide a catalog of the Hodges collection, with some bibliographical information. We did consider assigning bibliographical numbers to make this catalog the beginning of a Congreve bibliography, but because of the limitations of the collection, particularly in poetry, we realized that this would not be feasible. And such an attempt would have delayed even further a project at least partly commemorative. Yet we believe that this catalog will be of some value.

We have described the idiosyncrasies of particular copies, not ideal copy. We have not examined other copies. For example, in the Hodges copy of the third volume of the 1710 *Works of William Congreve* the dedicatory epistle to Lord Halifax has been bound between the section title and the contents list—improperly placed in terms both of the order indicated on the contents list and the signatures, but whether this is typical of the edition we do not know. However, we have attempted on the basis of the textual notes of certain modern editors, particularly Summers and Davis, to record some variants where bibliographical inferences can be reasonably made.

In presenting our descriptions, we have adopted basically the system of descriptive bibliography evolved by W. W. Greg and Fredson Bowers in Greg's *Bibliography of the English Printed Drama to the Restoration* and Bowers's *Principles of Bibliographical Description* and exemplified by Bowers and Richard Beale Davis (*George Sandys, a Bibliographical Catalogue of Printed Editions in England to 1700* [New York, 1950]) insofar as that system is consistent with our purpose.

In compiling the catalog, we determined to use 1800 as the terminal date for two reasons: the end of the eighteenth century marked the end of a particular period of Congreve's reputation and popularity; although the Hodges collection contains most twentieth-century editions of Congreve, it contains relatively few nineteenth-century ones—Leigh Hunt's and A. W. Ewald's editions of the collected plays but no editions of individual ones.

We have arranged the items in the catalog in chronological order according to the first publication of the individual work. Thus the first item listed is *Incognita* (1692), although the only separate Restoration or eighteenth-century edition of it in the Hodges collection is that of 1713. Each item—whether a distinct edition, a different issue, or a duplicate—has been numbered. These numbers have been adopted for reference purposes within this catalog. We have listed together all separate publications of the individual works. We have followed the catalog of individual works with the editions of the collected poems, the dramatic works, and the collected works, and finally with a list of Congreveana. Our definition of a collected edition is a volume with a general title page. Thus we have included the 1735 Tonson edition of the plays among the collected editions even though the plays are signed and paged separately. On the same principle we have excluded from the collected editions a volume of plays, all signed and paged separately and all published in 1774 by W. Fox, because the volume has no general title. Volumes which have a general title but which contain plays by authors other than Congreve have been included in the catalog of individual works.

In describing items which were designed to be published both separately and as part of a collected edition, we have provided a full description in the collected edition entry, although the individual entry is listed first. Our justification for this procedure is that the whole would be more comprehensible as a bibliographical entity if all of the data were provided there; the part, the individual play published separately, can be easily understood and its relationship to the whole, the collected edition, grasped through an examination of the cross reference.

Titles have been given in quasi-facsimile, although we have ignored the presence of broken letters and ligatures and occasional erratic positioning of type within the line. Swash capitals have been ignored in titles and elsewhere except, as in running-titles, where their use aids in distinguishing different typesetters of a particular edition or the portions of an edition which have been reset. Even there because swash type has not been available we have noted the presence of the swash capital thus: [swash]. Within the transcriptions words have been divided only where they were divided in the originals, and this division we have noted by a single vertical bar. We have throughout the catalog followed the English system of punctuation because of its greater clarity: we have used single quotation marks for direct quotation, and we have included within the quotation marks only the punctuation of the original; terminal punctuation of our addition will always be outside the quotation marks. Titles in black and red have been so described with the red portion underscored. Section titles within collected editions have been described in detail because they are frequently title pages of separate printings of the plays and because frequently they are a major indication of the line of descent. It has not been feasible to distinguish the size of capitals.

In the presentation of the collational formula we have attempted to follow the system of Greg and Bowers. It has been necessary occasionally to use an odd number to indicate the number of leaves in a terminal gathering when the leaves cannot logically be inferred. In noting prefatory and concluding leaves, we have preferred to err on the conservative side. We have included such leaves in the collational formula when they are possibly conjugate and when on the basis of the single copy we cannot determine that they are binders' leaves. We have not noted the absence of signatures or of volume numbers in the signature-line on pages where they would normally not appear, but we have noted their presence when they would normally not appear. The position and typography of page numbers has been noted only for the quartos appearing prior to the 1710 edition of the *Works* or when there are changes within an edition.

In the description of the contents we have indicated whether a cast is listed on the dramatis personae page. Unless we have indicated otherwise, the cast is always the cast listed in the first quarto. We have generally followed Greg's practice in describing ornaments. Ornaments which appear on the title page, headpieces to dedicatory epistles, tailpieces following prologues, the last act of a play, and epilogues, and ornaments forming part of the headtitle have been described and their size in millimeters given. Although we have noted the presence of ornamental initials and factotums, we have not described them and have given their size only when they begin dedicatory epistles, prologues, the first acts of plays, and epilogues. Because many of the Congreve editions were published by Tonson—uncle, nephew, or grandnephews—we have described and numbered those ornaments in an appendix (Appendix A). Within the description of the contents the ornament will be referred to by its number preceded by T (for Tonson). Since Baskerville's ornaments have frequently been reproduced, we have simply identified the single ornament used in his 1761 edition of Congreve as Baskerville 1, the num-

ber which it bears on the sheet of type specimens issued by the Baskerville press in the 18th century.

Although we have been selective in our reproduction of catchwords, we
have attempted to record all variants—i.e., all instances in which the
word on the following page is not identical in every way with the catchword. We have recorded press figures whenever they are present, and
normally in late eighteenth-century editions we have noted their absence.

To facilitate identification of the actual copies that we have used, we
have provided the call numbers assigned by The University of Tennessee
Library.

Finally we have supplemented this catalog of Congreve editions with
an appendix containing the titles in quasi-facsimile of items in the Hodges
collection which duplicate precisely or approximately books within
Congreve's own library. This collection, although secondary to Dr.
Hodges's collection of Congreve editions, was central to his interest in
Congreve. As the discoverer and editor of Congreve's book list, he recognized the value of that list in providing a basis for studying Congreve's
intellectual interests and development and attempted to bring together a
counterpart of Congreve's own library to make such a study possible.
It seems appropriate to include those items as an appendix to this catalog.

We should like to acknowledge our gratitude to The University of
Tennessee Library and to the administrators of the Hodges Better English Fund for their generous financial support and to the Graduate School
of The University of Tennessee, which by a faculty grant freed Mr.
Lyles from other duties for several months to work on the project. We
should like to thank particularly Mr. William Jesse and Miss Olive
Branch of the Library and Professors Kenneth Knickerbocker and
Richard Beale Davis of the English Department for their encourage-
ment. Professor Norman Sanders has rescued us more than once from
the Slough of Despond and has saved us more than once from error. But
for the errors which remain he bears no responsibility. Finally to the
clerical staff of the library's Special Collections who have labored long
and endured much we offer thanks.

# ABBREVIATIONS USED IN
# THE CATALOG AND APPENDICES

| | |
|---|---|
| Avery | Emmett L. Avery, *Congreve's Plays on the Eighteenth-Century Stage*. New York, 1951. |
| Case | Arthur E. Case, *A Bibliography of English Poetical Miscellanies 1521–1750*. Oxford, 1935. |
| Congreve | John C. Hodges, *The Library of William Congreve*. New York, 1955. |
| Gaskell | Philip Gaskell, *John Baskerville: A Bibliography*. Cambridge, 1959. |
| Halkett and Laing | Samuel Halkett and John Laing, *Dictionary of Anonymous and Pseudonymous English Literature*. Edited James Kennedy, W. A. Smith, and A. F. Johnson. Edinburgh, 1926. |
| Hodges | John C. Hodges, ed. *William Congreve: Letters and Documents*. New York, 1964. |
| Macdonald | Hugh Macdonald, *John Dryden: A Bibliography of Early Editions and of Drydeniana*. Oxford, 1939. |
| Pforzheimer | *The Carl H. Pforzheimer Library: English Literature 1475–1700*. New York, 1940. |
| Plomer | Henry R. Plomer, *English Printers' Ornaments*. London, 1924. |
| Sale | William Merritt Sale, Jr., *Samuel Richardson: Master Printer*. Ithaca, 1950. |
| Stone | George Winchester Stone, ed. *The London Stage 1660–1800. Part 4: 1747–1776*. Carbondale, 1962. |
| Stonehill | Charles A. Stonehill, Jr., Andrew Block, and H. Winthrop Stonehill, *Anonyma and Pseudonyma*. 2nd edition. London, 1927. |
| Stratman | Carl J. Stratman, *Bibliography of English Printed Tragedy 1565–1900*. Carbondale and Edwardsville, 1966. |
| W & M | Gertrude L. Woodward and James G. McManaway, compilers. *A Check List of English Plays 1641–1700*. Chicago, 1945. |
| Wing | Donald T. Wing, compiler. *Short-Title Catalogue of Books Printed in England, Scotland, Ireland, Wales, and British America and of English Books Printed in Other Countries 1641–1700*. New York, 1945. |

# THE CATALOG

*Incognita.* 1692

## 1. 1713

[within double rules] *INCOGNITA:* | OR, | LOVE | AND | DUTY | RECONCIL'D. | A | NOVEL. ‖ By Mr. CONGREVE. ‖ *LONDON,* | Printed for *R. Wellington* at the *Dolphin* and | *Crown* in St. *Paul's* Church-yard, 1713. | [outside double rule] [hand pointing to right] The Lovers Secretary: Or, The Adventures of *Lindamira,* | a Lady of Quality, written with her own Hand to her Friend | in the Country in 24 Letters, being a very entertaining History. | Price 2 *s.*

*Collation:* 8°. A⁵ B-F⁸ G³, 48 leaves, pp. [10] 1–64 81–101 *102* [=86] [misprinting 49 as 94], $4 (-A3 [signed on verso], A4, G3) signed.

HT] ‖ ‖ *INCOGNITA:* | OR, | LOVE and DUTY | RECONCIL'D.

*Contents:* A1: title (verso blank). A2: ‖ ‖ 'TO THE | Honoured and Worthily Eſteem'd | Mrs. *Katharine Leveſon.*' signed on A3ᵛ: *'CLEOPHIL.'* A4: ‖ ‖ 'THE | PREFACE | TO THE | READER.' B1: HT with text (cap⁴). G3ᵛ: *'BOOKS ſold by* R. Wellington *at the* Dolphin | *and* Crown, *in St.* Paul's Church-yard.'

RT] *Love and Duty Reconcil'd.* [*Reconcil'd.* with swash R on $1ʳ⁻ᵛ, 3, 8, except gathering A and B1 and G1ʳ⁻ᵛ]

CW] A5 *IN-* B2 (Divertiſe-) ments, [ments;] C1 Fa- ['Father,] D5ᵛ Diſ- [Diſobedience,] E6 (ſays ['(ſays] F8 Con- [Condition.]

*Type:* text (B3): 33 ll., 154(166) x 90 mm., 92R.

*Notes:* Page numbers in headline against outer margin of type page. Bound in marbled brown boards with brown leather over the spine. Purchased in 1957. Pforzheimer 199.

PR3364 .I5 1713

## *The Eleventh Satire of Juvenal* and *To Mr. Dryden on His Translation of Persius.* 1693

## 2. 1693

[within double rules] THE | SATIRES | OF | Decimus Junius Juvenalis.

| Tranſlated into | ENGLISH VERSE. ‖ By | Mr. *DRYDEN*, | AND | Several other Eminent Hands. ‖ Together with the | SATIRES | OF | Aulus Perſius Flaccus. ‖ Made Engliſh by Mr. *Dryden*. ‖ With Explanatory Notes at the end of each SATIRE. ‖ To which is Prefix'd a Diſcourſe concerning the Original and Progreſs | of SATIRE. Dedicated to the Right Honourable *Charles* Earl of | *Dorſet*, &c. By Mr. *DRYDEN*. ‖ *Quicquid agunt homines, votum, timor, Ira, voluptas,* | *Gaudia, diſcurſus,* *noſtri eſt farrago libelli*. ‖ *LONDON,* | Printed for *Jacob* Tonſon at the *Judge*'s-*Head* in *Chancery-Lane*, near | *Fleetſtreet* M DC XCIII. ‖ Where you may have Compleat Sets of Mr. *Dryden*'s Works, in Four Volumes | in Quarto, the Plays being put in the order they were Written.

*Half-title:* *A1*: ‖ THE | SATIRES | OF | JUVENAL, | AND | PERSIUS. ‖

*Section-title,* ²*A*¹: [within double rules] THE | SATIRES | OF | Aulus Perſius | Flaccus. ‖ Made *ENGLISH* | By | Mr. *DRYDEN*. ‖ *Sæpius* *in Libro memoratur Perſius uno* | *Quam levis in tota Marſus Amazonide.* | Mart. ‖ *LONDON,* | Printed for *Jacob Tonſon* at the *Judges Head* in *Chancery-* | *Lane,* near *Fleet-ſtreet.* 1693.

*Collation:* 2°. π¹ A²a–o² B–4L² ²A² ²B–²Z², 235 leaves, pp. [vi] i–liii *liv–lvi* 1–16 *17* 18–29 *30–31* 32–54 *55* 56–70 *71* 72–84 *85* 86–126 *127* 128–144 *145* 146–174 *175* 176–188 *189* 190–216 *217* 218–238 *239* 240–247 *248* 249–251 *252–253* 254–272 *273* 274–294 *295* 296–307 *308–309* 310–315 *316;* [4] ²1 2–18 *19* 20–28 *29* 30–44 *45* 46–56 *57* 58–74 *75* 76–87 *88* [misprinting xlii as lii, liii as xxxix, 140 as 141, 294 as 296] $1 signed.

*Contents:* π1ʳ⁻ᵛ: blank. *A1:* half-title (verso blank). *A2:* title (verso blank). a1: ‖ ‖ 'TO THE | Right Honourable | CHARLES, | Earl of *Dorſet* and *Middleſex,* | Lord Chamberlain of Their Maje- | ſties Houſehold: Knight of the | Moſt Noble Order of the | GARTER, *&c.*' (init. T⁵ [19 x 23]). Signed on o1: 'JOHN DRYDEN.' o1ᵛ: blank. o2: ‖ ‖ 'A | TABLE | TO | JUVENAL.' On o2ᵛ: ‖ 'The TABLE to PERSIUS.' Below: ‖ 'ERRATA.' B1–4L2: text of the satires. ²*A1:* section-title (verso blank) ²*A2:* ‖ ‖ 'To | Mr. DRYDEN, | ON HIS | TRANSLATION | OF | PERSIUS.' | [42 ll. 'A³S *when of Old* *Heroique Story tells*']. Signed on ²*A2*ᵛ: 'Will. Congreve.' ²B1–²Z²: text of the satires.

RT] ‖ *The DEDICATION.* ‖ a1ᵛ–o1; ‖ JUVENAL. ‖ B1ᵛ–4L2; ‖ PERSIUS. ‖ ²B1ᵛ–²Z2.

CW] f1 underſtood: [underſtood.] E1 *Explana-* [EXPLANATORY] I1 THE [I1ᵛ blank] O1ᵛ Anwſer [Anſwer] P1 15 *Romulus,* [15 *Romulus;*] S2ᵛ [9 *Palphurius,*

[9 *Palphurius*] 2O2ᵛ THE EIGHT [THE EIGHTH] 2P2 Ye [Yet] 3R2 EXPLANA- [3R2ᵛ blank] 3S2 THE [3S2ᵛ blank] 4H1 For [(For] 4I2 THE [4I2ᵛ blank] 4L2 THE [verso blank] ²B2 THE [ARGUMENT] ²R1ᵛ Nature [CORN.] [no CW on Y1ᵛ, 2U1ᵛ, 3B1ᵛ, 3U2ᵛ, 4E2, 4I1, 4L1ᵛ]

*Type:* dedication (a2): 53 ll., 246(271) x 128 mm., 93R. text (D1): 27 ll., 241(276) x 127 mm., 180R.

*Notes:* Page numbers in headline against outer margins of type-page. In the headline against the inner margin of the type-page 'Sat. I.' and according to number in rom. numbers except 'Sat [no period] (2A1ᵛ, 4B2ᵛ) and 'Sat. IX. [for XIV.] on 4E1. Each Juvenalian satire is preceded by a half-title and an argument and is followed by explanatory notes. The typography of the 'Argument *of the firſt Satyr.*' (B1ᵛ) differs from that of the remaining arguments. The eighth satire has an advertisement (2U2) preceding the explanatory notes; the typography of the half-title changes with the eleventh satire. Each of the satires of Persius is preceded by a half-title and an argument and followed by an explanatory note. Congreve translated Juvenal's eleventh satire (3K2-301) and wrote the dedicatory poem to Dryden on his translation of Persius. As has been frequently noted, the volume actually appeared in 1692. Bound in maroon cloth. Wing J1288, Macdonald 30a.

PA6447 .E5D7 1693

## *THE Old Bachelor.* 1693

### 3. 1693

THE | Old Batchelour, | A | COMEDY. | As it is ACTED at the | Theatre Royal, | By | Their MAJESTIES Servants. ‖ Written by Mr. *Congreve.* ‖ *Quem tulit ad Scenam ventoſo gloria Curru,* | *Exanimat lentus Spectator; ſedulus inflat.* | *Sic leve, ſic parvum eſt, animum quod laudis avarum* | *Subruit, aut reficit——* | [to the right] Horat. Epiſt. I. Lib. II. ‖ *LONDON,* | Printed for *Peter Buck,* at the Sign of the *Temple* | near the *Temple-gate* in *Fleet-ſtreet,* 1693.

*Collation:* 4°. A⁴ a² B-H⁴, 34 leaves, pp. [*12*] 1–55 *56;* $2 (-a2) signed.

HT] ‖ ‖ THE | Old Batchelour. ‖

*Contents:* A1: title (verso blank). A2: '*To the Right Honourable,* Charles *Lord* Clifford | *of* Lanesborough *&c.*' signed on A2ᵛ '𝔚𝔦𝔩𝔩. ℭ𝔬𝔫𝔤𝔯𝔢𝔟𝔢.' A3: 'To Mr. *CONGREVE.*' | [43 ll. '*W²HEN Vertue in purſuit of Fame appears,*'] signed 'THO. SOUTHERNE.' A3ᵛ: '*To Mr.* CONGREVE.' | [33 ll. 'T²He Danger's great in theſe cenſorious days,'] signed on A4 '*J. W. MARSH.*' ‖. A4ᵛ: '*To Mr. CONGREVE,* on his PLAY, | called, The *OLD BATCHELOR.*' | [24 ll. 'W²IT, *like true Gold, refin'd from all* | (*Allay,*'] signed on a1 'BEVIL HIGGINS.' ‖ ‖. a1ᵛ: '*PROLOGUE intended for the old Btcahe-* | *lour, ſent to the Author, by an unknown Hand.*' | [32 ll. 'M²OST Authors on the Stage at firſt appear'] a2: 'PROLOGUE | Spoken by Mrs. *Bracegirdle.*' | [27 ll. '*H²OW this vile World is chang'd! In former days,*'] a2ᵛ: 'Perſonæ Dramatis.' (with cast) B1: HT with text (cap³) headed 'ACT I. SCENE I. The Street.' H4ᵛ: 'EPILOGUE, | Spoken by Mrs. *Barry.*' | [30 ll. '*A²S a raſh Girl, who will all Hazards run,*'].

CW] A4ᵛ *VVhat* [*What*] a2 Dra- [Perſonæ] A3ᵛ *But* [But] B2ᵛ Com- [company] D2 *Lucy:* [*Lucy.*] E3ᵛ *Læ.* [*Læt.*] F4ᵛ: *Læt.* G2 Heart- [Heart-well]

*Type:* text (B1ᵛ): 43 ll. 172(184) x 118 mm., 81R.

*Notes:* Page numbers are centered in parentheses B-E4ᵛ and in brackets F-H4. No RT. The title page is badly stained with the 'e' and 'oy' in 'Theatre Royal' partially rubbed out. Bound in brown cloth with marbled paper inset. W & M 240. Wing C5863.

PR3364 .O5 1693

## 4.  1693

[*title*] like 1693 (3.) except for . . . | [to the right] Horat. Epiſt. I. Lib. II. ‖ 𝕿𝖍𝖊 𝕱𝖔𝖚𝖗𝖙𝖍 𝕰𝖉𝖎𝖙𝖎𝖔𝖓, 𝕮𝖔𝖗𝖗𝖊𝖈𝖙𝖊𝖉. ‖ *LONDON,* | Printed for *Peter Buck,* at the Sign of the *Temple* | near the *Inner-Temple-gate* in *Fleet-ſtreet,* 1693.

*Collation:* 4°. A⁴ a² B-H⁴, 34 leaves, pp. [*12*] 1–55 *56;* $2 (-a2) signed.

HT] as in 1693 (3.)

*Contents:* A1: title (verso blank). A2: dedicatory epistle. A3: Southerne's commendatory poem. A3ᵛ: commendatory poem signed on A4 '*J. MARSH.*' A4ᵛ: Higgons' commendatory poem. a1ᵛ: anonymous prologue. a2: prologue. a2ᵛ: dramatis personae (with cast). B1: HT with text (cap³). H4ᵛ: epilogue.

CW] A3ᵛ *But* [But] A4ᵛ *VVhat* [*What*] B2ᵛ Com- [Company] C1 *Sharper.* [*Sharp.*] C4ᵛ in- [indefatigable] D1ᵛ ACT. [ACT] D3 *Sett.* [*Setter.*] D3ᵛ *Lucy.* [*Lucy,*] E4 Nykin [*Nykin--*] F4ᵛ *Læt.* G2 *Heart.* [Heart-well]

*Type:* text (B1ᵛ): 43 ll. 175(185) x 119 mm., 81R.

*Notes:* Page numbers are centered in the headline in parentheses B-F⁴, in brackets G-H⁴. No RT. Portion of a2 below CW is torn off. The error in 'Batchelor' in the title of the anonymous prologue has been corrected. Bound in red cloth. W & M 243. Wing C5866. Purchased in 1939.

PR3364. O5 1693a

## 5. 1694

[*title*] like 1693 (3.) except for . . . | Theatre-Royal, | [2 lines] ‖ [1 line] ‖ [5 lines] ‖ *LONDON*, | Printed for *P. Buck,* and are to be ſold by | *James Knapton,* at the *Crown* in St. *Pauls* | Church-yard. M DC XCIV. | *ADVERTISEMENT.* | THE Memoirs of Monſieur *de Pontis,* who ſerved in the *French* Armies ſix and fifty | Years, under *Henry* IV. *Lewis* XIII. and *Lewis* XIV. Kings of *France.* Contain- | ing many remarkable paſſages relating to the [cropped] the Court and the [cropped]

*Collation:* 4°. A-H⁴, 32 leaves, pp. [*10*] 1–51 *52–54;* $2 signed.

HT] as in 1693 (3.)

*Contents:* A1: title (verso blank) A2: dedicatory epistle. A3: Southerne's commendatory poem. A3ᵛ: commendatory poem signed '*J. D. MARSH.*' A4: Higgons' commendatory poem. A4ᵛ: anonymous prologue. B1: prologue. B1ᵛ: dramatis personae (with cast). B2: HT with text (cap⁴) H3ᵛ: epilogue. H4: ‖ ‖ 'BOOKS Sold by *James Knapton,* at the | *Crown* in St. *Paul's* Church-yard.'

CW] B4ᵛ *Bell.* C1ᵛ Sir *Jo.* [Sir *J* [swash] *o.*] C2 Sir *J* [swash] *o.* [Sir *Jo.*] C4: *Belin.* Pish [*Belind.* Pish,] D3 forget- [forgetting] E1ᵛ *Silv.* Nay, [*Silv.* Nay] E3 *Fond. I* profeſs [*Fond.* I profeſs] F1 *SCENE* [SCENE] F3 *Læt.* Then, [*Læt.* Then] F3ᵛ *Læt.* 'Tis [*Let.* 'Tis] F4 *Læt.* Ra- [*Let.* Rather,] G2 *Setter.* [*Sett.*] G3 *Setter* I war- [*Setter. I* warrant] H4 Mr. *Shadwell's*ss [Mr. *Shadwell's*]

*Type:* text (B2ᵛ): 45 ll. 186(199) x 118 mm., 83R.

*Notes:* Page numbers are centered in parentheses in the headline. CW frequently printed on the last line of type, the first instance occurring on C3. No RT. Bound in green cloth. W & M 245. Wing C5868.

PR3364 .O5 1694

## 6. 1694

[*title*] as in 1694 (5.) except that less material is cropped from the advertisement . . . Contain- | ing many remarkable paſſages relating to the War, the Court, and the Government of | [cropped]

*Notes:* Another copy. Imperfect; gathering C and leaves H3.4 are missing. Leaf H2, loose, does not seem to belong to this copy. Purchased from R. J. Dobell in 1956.

PR3364 .O5 1694a

## 7. 1694

[*title*] as in 1694 (5.) except for . . . | *LONDON,* | Printed for *James Knapton,* at the *Crown* in | St. *Pauls* Church-yard. M DC XCIV. [etc. as in 5. except that two lines of the advertisement are cropped]

*Notes:* Since the difference in the imprints of 5. and 7. seems to be a press-alteration rather than the result of a cancellans title-page, 7. is apparently another state of the same issue rather than a re-issue. W & M 247. Wing C5869. Bound in red cloth.

PR3364 .O5 1694b

## 8. 1697

THE | Old Batchelour, | A | COMEDY. | As it is ACTED at the | Theatre-Royal, | By | His Majesty's　Servants. ‖ Written　by　Mr. *CONGREVE.* ‖ The Sixth Edition Corrected. ‖ [4-line motto from Horace and 1-line ack.] ‖| *LONDON,* | Printed for *Peter Buck,* at the Sign of the *Temple* in *Fleet-* | *ſtreet,* over againſt *Chancery-Lane-End,* 1697.

*Collation:* 4°. A-H⁴, 32 leaves, pp. [*10*] 1–51 *52–54;* $2 signed.

HT] as in 1694 (5.)

*Contents:* A1: title (verso blank). A2: dedicatory epistle. A3: Southerne's commendatory poem. A3ᵛ: commendatory poem signed 'J. *Marſh.*' A4: commendatory poem signed 'Bevil. Higgons.' A4ᵛ: anonymous prologue. B1: prologue. B1ᵛ: dramatis personae (with cast). B2: HT with text. (cap⁴) H3ᵛ: epilogue. H4: ‖ ‖ '*Books and Plays lately Printed, and Sold by* Peter Buck, | *at the Sign of the* Temple *in* Fleetſtreet; *and* Richard | Wellington, *at the* Lute *in St.* Paul's *Church-yard.*'

CW] A4ᵛ: PRO- [PROLOGUE] B4 Who [who] C4 *Belin.* Piſh. [*Belind.* Piſh,] D3 forget- [forgetting] D4ᵛ *Sharp.* Hearkee, [*Sharp.* Harkee,] E1ᵛ *Silv.* Nay, [*Silv.* Nay] F4 *Læt.* Ra- [*Læt.* Rather,] G4ᵛ *Aram.* You.

*Type:* text (B2ᵛ): 45 ll. 182(193) x 118 mm., 81R.

*Notes:* Page numbers are centered in parentheses in the headline. No RT. The closeness of the text would suggest that this was set from 5.; the different line endings justify the labelling of it as a new edition. This is the first edition in the Hodges collection in which Higgons' name has been spelled correctly. Bound in red cloth. W & M 248; Wing C5870.

PR3364 .O5 1697

## 9. 1707

THE | Old Batchelor. | A | COMEDY. | As it is ACTED at the | THEATRE ROYAL, | BY | Her MAJESTY'S Servants. || Written | by Mr. *CONGREVE.* || THE SEVENTH EDITION. || [4-line motto from Horace and 1-line ack.] || *LONDON,* | Printed for *R. W.* and Sold by *Egbert Sanger,* at the Poſt- | Houſe near the *Temple*-Gate in *Fleetſtreet,* 1707. | *Where may be had all Sorts of Plays.*

*Half-title,* A1: || THE | Old Batchelor. | A | COMEDY. ||

*Collation:* 4°. *A*⁴ B-H⁴ ²H⁴, 36 leaves, pp. [*12*] 1–36 39–58 *59–62* [=60]; $2 (−A2) signed.

*Contents:* A1: half-title (verso blank). A2: title (verso blank) A3: dedicatory epistle. A4: Southerne's commendatory poem. On A4ᵛ: Marsh's commendatory poem. On B1: Higgons' commendatory poem. B1ᵛ: anonymous prologue. B2: prologue. B2ᵛ: dramatis personae (with cast). B3: HT with text. (cap⁵) ²H3: epilogue. ²H3ᵛ: || || '*PLAYS Sold by* Egbert Sanger, *at the* | *Poſt-Houſe near* Temple-Bar.' On ²H4: 'BOOKS *ſold by* Egbert Sanger.' On ²H4: '*PLAYS.*'

CW] A4ᵛ *So* B1ᵛ *PRO-* [PROLOGUE,] C4ᵛ raſcally D4ᵛ *Bell.* E4ᵛ *Enter* F4ᵛ Sir G4 *Læt.* In- [*Læt.* Indeed,] H4 *Enter* [(*Enter*)]

*Type:* text (B4): 45 ll. 185(195) x 115 mm., 82R.

*Notes:* Page numbers are centered in the headline in brackets B3-F4ᵛ and in parentheses G1-²H2ᵛ. No RT. Gatherings G, H, and ²H were set by a different compositor. Bound in red cloth.

PR3364 .O5 1707

## 10. 1707

*Notes:* A copy added to the Tennessee library after Dr. Hodges's death. Unbound. Purchased from Dawson's, 1968.

PR3364 .O5 1707 cop. 2

## 11. 1710

[within double rules] FIVE | PLAYS, | Written by | Mr. *CONGREVE*. | *VIZ.* | [four lines braced to the right] *The Old Batchelor,* | *The Double-Dealer,* | *The Way of the World,* | *Love for Love,* | COMEDIES. | *The Mourning-Bride,* A TRAGEDY. || *LONDON:* | Printed and Sold by *H. Hills,* in *Black-* | *Fryars,* near the *Water-fide.* 1710.

*Section-title,* A1: THE | Old Batchelour. | A | COMEDY. | As it is ACTED at the | THEATRE ROYAL, | BY | Her MAJESTY'S Servants. || Written by Mr. *CONGREVE.* || [4-line motto from Horace and 1-line ack.] || *LONDON:* | Printed and Sold by *H. Hills,* in *Black-* | *Fryars,* near the *Water-fide.*

*Collation:* 12°. π1 A-C¹²D⁴, 41 leaves, pp. [2] *1–2* 3–80; $5 (-D3, D4) signed.

*Notes:* A separate binding of *The Old Bachelor* which is identical with the type setting of the play in Hills' 1710 edition of the plays. See item 100.

PR3364 .O5 1710

## 12. 1733

[*title*] like *Old Bachelor* section-title of 1733 ed. of *Dramatick Works.*

*Notes:* Except for the presence of the stub of a cancellandum between gatherings A and B, this edition of the play is identical with that printed in the 1733 *Dramatick Works* (102.) A12ᵛ and B1 are identical with A12ᵛ and B1 of the *Dramatick Works.* Bound in red cloth.

PR3364 .O5 1733

## 13. 1735

[in black and red]

[*title*] like *Old Bachelor* section-title of 1735 Tonson edition of the *Plays.*

*Notes:* A separate binding of the play as it appears in the 1735 edition of the *Plays.* See item 103. Bound in red cloth.

PR3364 .O5 1735

## 14. 1737

THE | Old Batchelor. | A | COMEDY. ‖ [4-line motto from Horace and 1-line ack.] ‖ Written by Mr. CONGREVE. ‖ [unbalanced floral orn. (16 x 31)] ‖‖ *DUBLIN:* | Printed for P. CRAMPTON, Bookſeller, at | *Addiſon's-Head,* over-againſt the *Horſe-guard* in | *Dame-ſtreet,* M DCC XXXVII.

*Collation:* 12°. A-C¹², 36 leaves, pp. *1–3* 4–71 *72;* $5 signed.

HT] [orn. (21 x 67): centered floral basket with winged figures on both sides clasping scrollwork, within ruled border] THE | OLD BATCHELOR. ‖

*Contents:* A1: title. A1ᵛ: [orn. (15 x 71) centered flaming heart with flowers and leaves] dramatis personae (without cast). A2: HT with text (fact⁷) C12ᵛ: 'BOOKS Printed for and Sold by PHILIP | CRAMPTON, Bookſseller, at *Addiſon's-* | head, oppoſite to the *Horſe-guard, Dame-* | ſtreet.'

RT] *The Old Batchelor.*

CW] A12ᵛ (ridicu-) lous, B3 *Set.* [*Setter.*] B7ᵛ *Fond,* [*Fond.*] C7 *Sharp.* [*Shap.*] C11 *Setter:* [*Setter.*] [no CW on C11ᵛ]

*Type:* text (A3): 42 ll., 136(144) x 71 mm., 64R.

*Notes:* The acts are not divided into scenes. There are no press figures. The acts are separated by rules. The book advertisement lists a Crampton edition of *The Dramatick Works of Mr. Congreve.*

PR3364 .O5 1737

## 15. 1754

[in black and red] [*title*] identical with *Old Bachelor* section-title of 1735 edition of *Plays* except for | Printed for J. and R. TONSON and S. DRAPER | in the *Strand.* | [partial rule] M̱ DCC ̱LIV.

*Collation:* 12°. A-C¹² D⁶ (D6 blank? missing), 41 leaves, pp. *1–7* 8–80 *81–82;* $5 signed (-D2.4.5)

HT] [orn. T3] THE | OLD BATCHELOR. ‖

*Contents:* A1: blank. A1ᵛ: engraved illustration. A2: title (verso blank). A3: prologue. A3ᵛ: dramatis personae (with cast). A4: HT with text (orn. initial⁶) D5: epilogue. On D5ᵛ orn. (T4).

RT] *The* OLD BATCHELOR.

CW] A12ᵛ the B12ᵛ SCENE C7 *Fond.* [*Læt.*]

*Type:* text (A5): 41 ll., 135(144) x 73, 66R.

*Notes:* This cheaply printed duodecimo omits all the prefatory material; the acts are separated by ornaments. The engraved illustration depicts the scene (III, 4) in which Silvia throws Heartwell's purse to the floor and pretends to weep at his proposal. The engraved surface measures 128 x 76 mm. and is signed on the left '*F. Hayman inv. et del.*' and on the right '*C. Grignion sculp.*' No press figures. Bound in red cloth.

PR3364 .O5 1754

## 16. 1774

THE | OLD    BATCHELOR. | A | COMEDY. | Written    by | *Mr.* CONGREVE. ‖ [4-line motto from Horace and 1-line ack.] ‖ [triang. fleuron type orn.] ‖ LONDON: | Printed for W. Fox, in *Holborn.* | [partial rule] | M DCC LXXIV.

*Collation:* 12°. *A*² B-D¹² E⁴, 42 leaves, pp. *1–11* 12–82 *83–84* (*4* misnumbered as 72), plate (opp. sig. *A1*) $5 (-E3.4) signed.

HT] ‖| THE | OLD BATCHELOR. ‖

*Contents: A1:* title (verso blank). *A2:* dedicatory epistle. B1: Southerne's commendatory poem. On B1ᵛ: Marsh's commendatory poem. On B2: Higgons' commendatory poem. B2ᵛ: Falkland's prologue. B3: prologue. B3ᵛ: dramatis personae (with cast). B4: HT with text. E4: epilogue (verso blank).

RT] *The* OLD BATCHELOR.

CW] B5ᵛ Buʃi- [Buʃineʃs]. C9 *Silv.* [*Sylv.*] D12ᵛ the

*Type:* text (B7), 42 ll., 140(147) x 73 mm., 66R.

*Notes:* Except for the omission of a 4-page life of Congreve this edition is identical with the text of the play published in a collection with Congreve's other plays and two plays of Rowe by Fox in 1774. See item 17. The play is divided into scenes. The title is preceded by a disjunct engraving, which from its date must have been added later. The engraving is headed '*ACT IIII* THE OLD BACHELOR. *Scene 22d*' and below '*Miss POPE in the Character of LETETIA.* | *Indeed & indeed now my dear Nykin--* | *I never saw this wicked man before.*' The engraved surface, with a triple rule border, measures 116 x 81 mm., and is signed on the engraved surface on the left '*Is. Roberts del. 1781*' and on the right '*Ias. Roberts sc.*' No press figures. Sewn. Brown paper cover glued on.

PR3364 .O5 1774

## 17.  1774

[*title*] as in 16.

*Collation:* 12°. $A^4$ B-$D^{12}$ $E^4$, 44 leaves, *1–2* i–iv *3–11* 12–82 *83–84* (4 misnumbered as 72) plate (opp. sig. *A1*); $5 (-E3.4) signed.

*Notes:* Except for the 4-page life of Congreve interpolated between the title and the dedicatory epistle this copy is identical with 16. It is bound with Congreve's other plays and two of Rowe's in the following order: *Old Bachelor, Double-Dealer, Love for Love, Mourning Bride, Way of the World, Jane Shore, Fair Penitent.* Each is preceded by a disjunct engraving; each has Fox's imprint and is dated 1774; each is signed and paged separately. Although the *Life* bears some resemblance to the life in the 7th ed. of the works, it is not identical with it. The spine bears the title 'CONGREVE'S | DRAMATIC | WORKS.' and below, '1774.'

PR3362 .F6 1774

## 18.  1776

THE | *OLD  BACHELOR.* | A | COMEDY. | WRITTEN  BY | Mr. CONGREVE. | Marked  with  the  Variations  in  the | MANAGER'S BOOK, | AT  THE | 𝕿𝖍𝖊𝖆𝖙𝖗𝖊-𝕽𝖔𝖞𝖆𝖑 𝖎𝖓 𝖙𝖍𝖊 𝕳𝖆𝖞-𝕸𝖆𝖗𝖐𝖊𝖙. | [4-line motto from Horace and ack.] | [triang. fleuron type orn.] | *LONDON:* | Printed for T. DAVIES; T. LOWNDES; T. CASLON; | W. NICOLL; and S. BLADON. | M.DCC.LXXVI.

*Collation:* 12°. A-$C^{12}$ $D^6$ (D6 blank? missing), 41 leaves, pp. *1–5* 6–80 *81–82* (56 misnumbered as 54); $5 (-D4.5) signed.

HT] THE | *OLD BACHELOR,* | A | COMEDY. ||

*Contents:* A1: title. A1$^v$: variations note. A2: prologue. A2$^v$: 'Dramatis Perſonæ, 1776, at the Hay-Market.' (with cast) [printed vertically]. A3: HT with text. D5: epilogue. D5$^v$: 'PLAYS *printed for* T. LOWNDES *and* | PARTNERS, *at* Six-pence *each.*'

RT] THE OLD BACHELOR. [BACHELOR (no period) A6, D4]

CW] A10ᵛ *Bluff.* [*Bluffe.*] B12 *Sharp.* (Sh printed upside down and reversed) [*Sharp.*] C12ᵛ *Heart* D1 in [*Sharp.*] D3 *Bluffe,* [*Bluffe;*]

*Type:* text (A7), 40 ll., 133(141) x 74 mm., 66R.

*Notes:* There is one press figure: D1ᵛ-2. The play is divided into scenes. Acts are separated by rules. As the title indicates, an acting version of the play. Bound in orange cloth. The cast does not correspond completely to any listed in Avery (*Congreve's Plays*) or Stone, although it is similar to the September 18, 1775 cast with the following differences: Sowdon as Heartwell, Lane as Sharper, Hamilton as Sir Joseph, Sparks as Bluffe, and Foote as Fondlewife. Stone lists Lane as playing Sharper.

PR3364 .O5 1776a

## 19. 1776

*BELL'S EDITION.* | [orn. partial rule] | THE | *OLD BATCHELOR.* | *A COMEDY, by Mr. CONGREVE.* | AS PERFORMED AT THE | 𝔗𝔥𝔢𝔞𝔱𝔯𝔢-𝔑𝔬𝔶𝔞𝔩 𝔦𝔫 𝔇𝔯𝔲𝔯𝔶-𝔏𝔞𝔫𝔢. | Regulated from the Prompt-Book, | *By PERMISSION of the MANAGERS,* | By Mr. HOPKINS, Prompter. | [4-line motto from Horace and ack.] | [John Bell's monogram] | *LONDON:* | Printed for JOHN BELL, near *Exeter-Exchange,* in the *Strand,* | and C. ETHERINGTON, at *York.* | [partial rule] | MDCCLXXVI.

*Collation:* 12°. A-G⁶, 42 leaves, pp. *1-2* 3-81 *82-84* plate (opp. sig A1); $3 signed.

HT] THE | OLD BATCHELOR. ‖

*Contents:* A1: title (verso blank). A2: prologue. A2ᵛ: dramatis personae (with cast). A3: HT with text. G5ᵛ: epilogue. G6: '*New Books publiſhed by* J. Bell.'

RT] THE OLD BATCHELOR. [BATCHELOR (no period) B5ᵛ]

CW] A2 Dramatis [DRAMATIS] B1 Me- [Methinks] C2ᵛ *Aram.* [\**Aram.*] C3 *Silv.* ['*Silv.*] D3 *Silv.* ['*Silv.*] E6ᵛ *Found.* [*stet*] F1 *Fond.* [A *Fond.*]

*Type:* text (B5), 40 ll., 132(141) x 71 mm., 66R.

*Notes:* This acting text is divided into scenes according to changes in setting. It has the following press figures: A6ᵛ-4, B6ᵛ-4, C4ᵛ-1, D6ᵛ-4, E3ᵛ-4, F1ᵛ-3, G1ᵛ-4. On $1 of each signed gathering in signature-line next fold 'VOL. II.' The title is preceded by a disjunct engraving headed '*ACT IV*. OLD BATCHELOR. *Scene IV*.' and below '*Mr. FOOTE in the Character of FONDLEWIFE. | Speak, I say have you consider'd what it is | to Cuckold your Husband?*' The engraved surface, within triple rules, measures 127 x 88 mm., and is signed on the left '*I. Roberts del*.' and on the right '*I. Thornthwayte Sc*.' Between the signatures, '*Publiſh'd for Bells Britiſh Theatre June the 4th. 1776*.' The cast listed does not correspond closely to any listed by Avery or Stone. Bound in orange cloth.

PR3364 .O5 1776

## 20. 1778

[*title*] as in 1776 (19.) except for | A COMEDY, | *As written by Mr. CONGREVE*, | AND . . . | [8 lines] | A NEW EDITION. | [John Bell's monogram] | *LONDON:* | Printed for JOHN BELL, near *Exeter-Exchange*, in the *Strand*. | [partial rule] | MDCCLXXVIII.

*Collation:* 12°. A-F⁶ G1, 37 leaves, pp. *1–2* 3–73 *74* plate (opp. sig. A1); $3 signed.

HT] as in 1776 (19.)

*Contents:* A1: title (verso blank). A2: prologue. A2ᵛ: dramatis personae (with cast as in 1776 [19.]). A3: HT with note on omitted lines and text. G1ᵛ: epilogue.

RT] as in 1776 (19.) except BATCHELOR [no period] B2, B4, C2ᵛ, E3ᵛ, F6.

CW] A6ᵛ (ſup-) porters B6ᵛ *Aram*. C5 can't [ſay] D6ᵛ *Aram*. E6ᵛ to F6ᵛ and *Type:* text (A4): 42 ll., 138(146) x 75 mm., 66R.

*Notes:* Like 19., an acting text. It has the following press figures: A5-2, B6ᵛ-2, C4-1, D1ᵛ-2, E1ᵛ-3, F6ᵛ-2. The disjunct engraving is identical with that in 1776 (19.) except that the scene number has been changed to arabic and the quotation below reads '*Speak I say*, . . .' and the signing on the right reads '*Thornthwaite S*.' The engraving is within double rules. Sewn. Glued in brown paper wrapper.

PR3364 .O5 1778

## 21. 1795

THE | *OLD BATCHELOR*. [partial double rule] | A | COMEDY, | BY MR. CONGREVE. | [partial double rule] | ADAPTED FOR | *THEATRICAL REPRESENTATION,* | AS PERFORMED AT

THE | THEATRE-ROYAL, DRURY-LANE. | [partial double rule] | REGULATED FROM THE PROMPT-BOOK, | *By Permission of the Manager.* ||| The Lines distinguished by inverted Commas, are omitted in the Representation. ||| LONDON: | [partial double rule] | *Printed for the Proprietors, under the Direction of* | JOHN BELL, 𝕭𝖗𝖎𝖙𝖎𝖘𝖍 𝕷𝖎𝖇𝖗𝖆𝖗𝖞, STRAND, | Bookseller to His Royal Highness the PRINCE of WALES | [partial rule] | MDCCXCV.

*Collation:* 12°. *A*² B-I⁶K², 52 leaves, pp. *1–5* 6–103 *104*, plate (opp. *A1*); $3 (-K2) signed.

HT] [orn. (15 x 53): comic mask imposed on horn and tambourine] THE | OLD BATCHELOR. |||

*Contents: A1:* title (verso blank). *A2:* prologue. *A2ᵛ:* dramatis personae (with cast as in 19.). B1: HT with text. K2ᵛ: epilogue.

RT] THE OLD BATCHELOR. [BATCHELLOR. D2; BATCHELOR (no period) D3ᵛ; BATCHELOR, D4]

*Type:* text (B3): 30 ll., 111(118) x 67 mm., 75R.

*Notes:* The edition has no catchwords; press figures are present as follows: D4-1, D5ᵛ-2, E1ᵛ-1, F3ᵛ-2, H4-2. The scene divisions are those of the 1776 ed. (19.). In the headline next to the fold '*Act I.*' and according to act. The disjunct engraving, preceding the title, is headed '*Act IV.* THE OLD BACHELOR. *Scene IV.*' and below '*Mr. FOOTE as FONDLEWIFE.* | *Bleſs us! What's the matter? What's the matter?* | London. Printed for J. Bell, Britiſh Library, Strand, May 15, 1795.' The engraved surface measures 116 x 78 mm., and is signed on the left '*Roberts del.*' and on the right '*Thornthwaite sculp.*' The play is the first play in a volume containing as well Cibber's *Lady's Last Stake*, Kelly's *False Delicacy*, and Farquhar's *Inconstant*. Each play is signed and paged separately; there is no general title. The volume is entitled on the spine 'EARLY | BRIT-ISH | COMEDYS' and below, '1795'.

PR1245 .B4 1795

## *THE Double-Dealer.* 1694

### 22. 1694

THE | Double-Dealer, | A | COMEDY. | Acted at the | *THEATRE ROYAL,* | By their Majeſties Servants. || Written by Mr. *CONGREVE.* || *Interdum tamen, & vocem Comœdia tollit.* | [to the right] Hor. Ar. Po. ||

*LONDON,* | Printed for *Jacob Tonſon,* at the *Judges-Head* near | the *Inner-Temple-Gate* in *Fleet-ſtreet.* 1694.

*Collation:* 4°. A⁴ a⁴ B-L⁴, 48 leaves, pp. *[16]* 1–79 *80;* $2 signed.

HT] ‖ ‖ THE | Double-Dealer. | A | COMEDY.

*Contents:* A1: title (verso blank). A2: ‖ ‖ 'To the Right Honourable | Charles Mountague, | ONE OF THE | Lords of the *TREASURY.*' (cap⁸) signed on a1ᵛ '*William Congreve.*' a2: ‖ ‖ 'To my Dear Friend | Mr. Congreve, | On His COMEDY, call'd, | The Double-Dealer.' | [79 ll. '*W³ELL then; the promis'd hour is come | at last;'*] signed on a3ᵛ 'John Dryden.' ‖ a4: 'PROLOGUE | Spoken by Mrs. *Bracegirdle.*' | [35 ll. '*M²Oors, have this way (as Story tells) to know'*]. a4ᵛ: 'Perſonæ Dramatis.' (with cast) B1: HT with text (cap⁴) headed ‖ 'ACT I. SCENE I.' ‖ L4ᵛ: 'EPILOGUE: Spoken by Mrs. | *Mountford.*' | [36 ll. '*C⁴Ould Poets but forſee how Plays would take,*]

RT] *The Double-Dealer.* [*Double-Dealer* (no period) L1; swash capitals T and D E-I4ᵛ, with other variants as noted: *The Double=Dealer* E4ᵛ, F2ᵛ; *The Double Dealer.* (no hyphen) E1, F3]

CW] A4ᵛ in a1ᵛ TO [To] a3ᵛ Prologue [PROLOGUE] B4ᵛ *Brisk.* C4 *L. Froth.* [*Ld. Froth.*] C4ᵛ *Ld. Froth.* [*Ld. Froth.*] D4 *Mask.* [*Maſ.*] E4ᵛ *Mel.* Why F4 Lady [(Lady] F4ᵛ *Cynth.* [*Cyn.*] G4ᵛ Lady H4ᵛ Subject, [Subject:] I1 Ld. [*Ld.*] I4ᵛ Lord [*Ld.*] K4ᵛ *Cynt.* [no CW on C3, I4]

*Type:* text (B2): 38 ll. 176(189) x 109 mm; 92R.

*Notes:* The page numbers are in the headline against the outer margin of the type-page except for 1 within brackets centered in the headline. Bound in brown leather. Purchased from Blackwell's, Oxford, in 1949. W & M 231; Wing C5847; Macdonald 31.

PR3364 .D7 1694

## 23. 1694

A different state.

*Collation:* 4°. A⁴ a⁴ B-G4 (±G1) H-L⁴, 48 leaves, pp. *[16]* 1–79 *80;* $2 signed.

*Type:* text (B2): 38 ll. 178(191) x 109 mm., 93R.

*Notes:* The cancellans G1 corresponds to the BY pattern described by Fredson Bowers ("The Cancel Leaf in Congreve's *'Double Dealer,'* 1694," *PBSA,*

XLIII (1949), 78–82) except that the variants on G1ᵛ in ll. 19, 30 read 'come ſee' | and *'plac'd,'*. 'kiſs and *Papa'* (G4ᵛ, 1. 27) corrected to 'and kiſs *Papa.'* Purchased in 1956. Bound in green cloth. W & M 231a.

PR3364 .D7 1694a.

## 24. 1706

THE | Double-Dealer. | A | COMEDY. | As it is Acted at the | *THEATRE ROYAL.* | By Their MAJESTIES Servants. ‖ Written by Mr. *CONGREVE.* ‖ *Interdum tamen, & vocem Comœdia tollit.* Hor. Ar. Po. | *Huic equidem Conſilio palmam do: hic me magnifice effero, qui vim* | *tantam in me & poteſtatem habeam tantæ aſtutiæ, vera dicendo* | *ut eos ambos fallam.* [to the right] Syr. in Terent. Heaut. ‖ The SECOND EDITION, Reviſed. ‖ *LONDON:* | Printed for *Jacob Tonſon;* and Sold by *James Knapton* at the | *Crown* in St. *Paul's* Church-yard, *George Strahan* over-againſt | the Royal Exchange in *Cornhill,* and *Egbert Sanger* at the | Poſt-Houſe near the *Temple*-Gate in *Fleetſtreet.* 1706.

*Collation:* 4°. A⁴ (A⁴ missing) B-I⁴ K², 37 leaves, pp. [*8*] 1–63 *64–66.* $2 (-E2, K2) signed.

HT] ‖ ‖ THE | Double-Dealer. ‖

*Contents:* A1: title (verso blank). A2: dedicatory epistle (cap³). B1: prologue (cap²). B1ᵛ: dramatis personae (with cast). B2: HT with text (cap³). K1ᵛ: epilogue (cap²). K2: '*BOOKS Printed for* Jacob Tonſon, *at* Grays- | Inn *Gate.'*

RT] The *Double-Dealer.* [*Double Dealer.* B2ᵛ. RT frequently partly removed by cropping.]

CW] A3ᵛ To [PROLOGUE] B4ᵛ *Brisk.* C4ᵛ Sir *Paul.* D4ᵛ ſo E1ᵛ [Mask- [[Maskwell] F4ᵛ L.*P.* G4ᵛ Ld. *T.* H4ᵛ (re-) nounce I2 Ld. *T.* [*Mask.*] [no CW G2ᵛ, K1ᵛ]

*Type:* text (C1): 42 ll. 198(210) x 123 mm., 94R.

*Notes:* The page numbers are in the headline against outer margin of type-page except for 1 within brackets centered in the headline. CW 'To' on A3ᵛ indicates that John Dryden's commendatory poem 'To My Dear Friend Mr. Congreve' followed on A4, as Pforzheimer 195 notes. Bound in blue cloth.

PR3364 .D7 1706

## 25. 1733

[title] identical with *Double-Dealer* section-title of 1733 *Dramatick Works* (102.) except for | DOUBLE-DEALER.

*Notes:* A separate binding of the text of the single play from the 1733 *Dramatick Works* (102.) This copy has a blank prefixed leaf. Bound in blue cloth.

PR3364 .D7 1733

## 26. 1735

[in black and red]

[title] identical with *Double-Dealer* section title of 1735 edition of *Plays* (103.)

*Notes:* The type setting of the play is identical with that of the 1735 edition of *Plays*. All of the characteristics of the *Plays* copy are present except that the 'S' in the catchword on D4 (*Plays*, $^2$D4) has printed. *The Double-Dealer* is bound with four other plays in the following order: Rowe's *Lady Jane Gray* (1741), Wycherley's *Plain Dealer* (1734), Southerne's *Oroonoko* (1763), *The Double-Dealer* (1735), Hughes's *Siege of Damascus* (1753). Each play is signed and paged separately; the volume has no general title. The title on the spine is 'BRITISH | THEATRE | VOL | IX'.

PR1245 .B8 1735

## 27. 1744

THE | Double-Dealer. | A | COMEDY. || [1-line motto from Horace and 1-line ack.; 3-line motto from Terence and 1-line ack.] || Written by Mr. *William Congreve*. || [orn. (16 x 24): female bust in scrollwork] |||| *DUBLIN:* | Printed for PHILIP CRAMPTON Bookſeller, oppoſite | the *Horſe-Guard* in *Dame's-ſtreet*, M DCC XLIV.

*Collation:* 12°. A-F⁶ G³, 39 leaves, pp. *1–2* 3–78 [74 misprinted as 47], $3 (-G3) signed.

HT] [row of fleurons] | THE | Double-Dealer. ||

*Contents:* A1: title. A1ᵛ: dramatis personae headed by orn. (5 x 71): flowers and vines. A2: HT with text (cap²) on G3ᵛ orn. [19 x 23]: lamp with foliage.

RT] The *Double-Dealer*.

CW] A6ᵛ young B6ᵛ in C6ᵛ Sir D2 Lady, [Lady] E6ᵛ He's F1ᵛ *Maſk.* [*Mask.*] F6ᵛ Maʃk [Mask.]

*Type:* text (B1): 42 ll., 140(147) x 71 mm., 66R.

*Notes:* This edition follows the scene division of the Tonson *Works.* Bound in blue cloth.

PR3364 .D7 1744


## 28. 1759

THE | DOUBLE-DEALER. | A | COMEDY. ‖ Written by ¦ Mr. WILLIAM CONGREVE. ‖ [1-line motto from Horace and ack.; 3-line motto from Terence and 1-line ack.] ‖ [orn. as on 1736 Dublin *Works* (113.) vol. 2, A6] ‖‖ DUBLIN: | Printed for G. and A. EWING, W. SMITH, J. EXSHAW, | and H. BRADLEY, Bookſellers, in *Dameſtreet.* | [partial rule] | M DCC LIX.

*Collation:* 12°. A-D¹², 48 leaves, pp. *1–15* 16–95 *96* [85 misprinted as 58], $5 signed.

HT] [orn. (17 x 77): floral urn in center, birds at sides] | THE | DOUBLE-DEALER. | [orn. (5 x 71): scrollwork]

*Contents:* A1: title (verso blank). A2: dedicatory epistle (cap³) headed by orn. [imitation of T 45 (25 x 76)]. A5ᵛ: Dryden's commendatory poem (cap²) headed by orn. [centered flower with vines. (5 x 71)] A7: prologue (cap²). A7ᵛ: dramatis personae. A8: HT with text (cap⁴). D12ᵛ: epilogue (cap²).

RT] *The* DOUBLE-DEALER.

CW] A12ᵛ (ado-) ration, B12ᵛ Lady C3ᵛ *Brisk.* [*Briſk.*] D1 *Mask.* [*Maſk.*] D6ᵛ *Mask.* [*Maſk.*]

*Type:* text (B9): 40 ll., 132(141) x 73 mm., 66R.

*Notes:* Acts separated by orns. This edition is a reprint, largely paginal, of the text of the play of the 1736 Dublin *Works* (113.). Bound in blue cloth.

PR3364 .D7 1759


## 29. 1774

THE | DOUBLE DEALER. | A | COMEDY. | Written by | *Mr.* CONGREVE. ‖ [1-line motto from Horace and 1-line ack.; 3-line motto from Terence and 1-line ack.] || [triangle of fleuron type orn.] || LONDON: | Printed for W. Fox, in *Holborn.* | [partial rule] | M DCC LXXIV.

*Collation:* 12°. A⁸ B-D¹², 44 leaves, pp. *1–13* 14–87 *88*, plate (opp. sig. A1), $5 (-A4.5) signed.

HT] |||| THE | *DOUBLE DEALER.* ||

*Contents:* A1: title (verso blank). A2: dedicatory epistle (cap²) headed by row of type orn. A4ᵛ: Dryden's commendatory poem (cap²) headed by row of type orn. A6: prologue (cap²) A6ᵛ: dramatis personae (with cast). A7: HT with text (cap²). D12ᵛ: epilogue (cap²) headed by row of star type orn.

RT] *The* DOUBLE DEALER. [DEALFR B1ᵛ, C12ᵛ]

CW] A8ᵛ *Care.* B12ᵛ DeſIgn C12ᵛ Sir

*Type:* text (B2): 40 ll., 136(147) x 74 mm., 70R.

*Notes:* The play is the second in a volume containing the five Congreve plays and Rowe's *Jane Shore* and *The Fair Penitent.* See 17. The acts are separated by rules. There are no press figures. The title page is preceded by a disjunct engraving headed '*Act* The DOUBLE DEALER. *Scene*' and below: '*Mr.* YATES *in the Character of Sr.* PAUL PLYANT. | *Gads bud! I am provok'd into a fermentation, as my | Lady Froth says; Was ever the like read of in Story!--*' The engraved surface, within triple rules, measures 118 x 82 mm., and is signed on the left '*Is Roberts del. 1781*' and on the right '*Ias. Roberts sc*'. A note on Dryden's poem identifies '*Tom* the Second' as Thomas Shadwell.

PR3362 .F6 1774

## 30. 1777

*BELL'S EDITION.* | [partial double rule] | THE | *DOUBLE DEALER.* | A COMEDY, | *As written by CONGREVE.* | DISTINGUISHING ALSO THE | VARIATIONS OF THE THEATRE, | AS PERFORMED AT THE | 𝕿𝖍𝖊𝖆𝖙𝖗𝖊=𝕽𝖔𝖞𝖆𝖑 𝖎𝖓 𝕯𝖗𝖚𝖗𝖞=𝕷𝖆𝖓𝖊. | Regulated from the Prompt-Book. | *By PERMISSION of the MANAGERS.* | By Mr. HOPKINS, Prompter. | [John Bell's monogram] | *LONDON:* | Printed for JOHN BELL, near *Exeter Exchange*, in the *Strand.* | [partial rule] | MDCCLXXVII.

*Collation:* 12°. A-G⁶, 42 leaves, pp. *1–2* 3–82 *83–84*, plate (opp. sig. A1), $3 signed.

HT] THE | DOUBLE DEALER.

*Contents:* A1: title (verso blank). A2: dedicatory epistle (cap²). A4: Dryden's commendatory poem (cap²). A5: prologue (cap²). A5ᵛ: dramatis personae (with cast headed *'Covent-Garden.'*). A6: HT, statement of omissions set off by rules, and text (cap²). On G5 a triangle of fleurons. G5ᵛ epilogue (cap²). G6: *'Books publiſhed by* J. Bell.'

RT] THE DOUBLE DEALER.

CW] A6ᵛ (to-mor-)row; B3 *Briſk.* [*Brisk.*] C6ᵛ (threa-) 'tened D6ᵛ *Mel.* ['*Mel.*] E6ᵛ could F6ᵛ *Mask.* G3ᵛ *Sir. P.* [*Sir P.*]

*Type:* text (B3): 42 ll., 139(147) x 75, 65R.

*Notes:* A prompt book edition with the material omitted in representation within single quotation marks. The following press figures are present: A4-4, B6ᵛ-4, C1ᵛ-3, D6-4, E6-1, F1ᵛ-3, G1ᵛ-4. The title is preceded by a disjunct engraving headed '*ACT I.* THE DOUBLE DEALER. *Scene 4.*' Below: '*Mr. Booth in the Character of LORD FROTH.* | *Now when I laugh, I always laugh alone.*' Within double rules, the engraved surface measures 130 x 91 mm., and is signed on the left '*Roberts del.*' and on the right '*D. Reading ſculp.*' Between the signatures '*Publiſh'd for Bells Britiſh Theatre, July 1777.*' The cast listed (A5ᵛ) differs markedly from that listed for the March 5, 1776 performance at Covent Garden, a benefit for Thomas Sheridan, by Stone. Except for Miss Dayes and Mr. Woodward, who are listed as playing Cynthia and Brisk, the cast seems to be a combination of the March 5 performance and the December 17 performance of the 1776–77 season. See Avery, p. 186.

PR3364 .D7 1777

## 31.  1797

THE | *DOUBLE DEALER.* | [partial double rule] | A | COMEDY, | BY WILLIAM CONGREVE, ESQ. | [partial double rule] | ADAPTED FOR | *THEATRICAL REPRESENTATION,* | AS PERFORMED AT THE | THEATRE-ROYAL, COVENT-GARDEN. | [partial double rule] | REGULATED FROM THE PROMPT-BOOK, | *By Permission of the Manager.* ||| The Lines distinguished by inverted Commas, are omitted in the Representation, | and those printed in Italics are Additions of the Theatres. ||| LONDON: | [partial double rule] | PRINTED FOR AND UNDER THE DIRECTION OF | G. CAWTHORN, BRITISH LIBRARY, STRAND. | [partial rule] | 1797.

*Collation:* 12°. A² B-K⁶ L⁴, 60 leaves, pp. *i–iii* iv–viii *ix* x–xi *xii* xiii *xiv 15* 16–118 *119* 120 [iv misprinted as v], plate (opp. sig. A1), $3 (-L3) signed.

HT] [orn. as in HT, 21.] THE DOUBLE DEALER. |||

*Contents:* A1: title (verso blank). A2: dedicatory epistle. B3: Dryden's commendatory poem. B4ᵛ: prologue. B5ᵛ: dramatis personae (with cast as in 30.). B6: HT with text. L4: epilogue.

RT] THE DOUBLE DEALER. [DEALER, F3]

*Type:* text (C2): 30 ll., 111(119) x 68 mm., 74R.

*Notes:* The edition has no catchwords; press figures are present as follows: F1ᵛ-2, H4-1, I4ᵛ-1, K6ᵛ-2. The scene divisions are those of Bell's 1777 ed. (30.). In the headline next to the fold '*Act I.*' and according to act. The title page is preceded by a disjunct engraving headed '*Act* III. THE DOUBLE DEALER. *Scene* I' and below, '*Mr. HARLEY as MASKWELL.* | -*Well, this double-dealing is a jewel* | *Here he comes now for me.*- | [one line cropped which may read 'LONDON. Printed for J. Bell British . . .']' The engraved surface measures 114 x 80 mm., and is signed on the left '*Wilde delin.*' and on the right '*Audinet sculp.*' The play is the last play in a volume containing as well Mrs. Centlivre's *A Bold Stroke for a Wife*, Goldsmith's *She Stoops to Conquer*, and Garrick's adaptation of Shirley's *The Gamesters*. Each play is signed and paged separately; there is no general title. The volume is entitled on the spine 'EARLY | BRITISH | COMEDIES' and dated 1791.

PR1245 .C3 1797

## *The Mourning Muse of Alexis.* 1695

### 32. 1695

[within a 7-mm. mourning border] THE | Mourning Muſe | OF | ALEXIS. | A | PASTORAL. | Lamenting the Death of our late Gracious | QUEEN MARY | Of ever Bleſſed Memory. | [mourning rule (4 mm.)] | By Mr. *CONGREVE.* | [mourning rule (4 mm.)] | *Infandum Regina Jubes renovare dolorem!* Virg. | [mourning rule (4 mm.)] | *LONDON:* | Printed for *Jacob Tonſon*, at the *Judge's Head*, | near the *Inner-Temple Gate* in *Fleetſtreet*. 1695.

*Collation:* 2°. A-C², 6 leaves, pp. [*2*] 1–10, A2, B1, C1 signed.

HT] [mourning rule (4 mm.)] THE | Mourning Muſe | OF | ALEXIS. | A | PASTORAL. ||

*Contents:* A1: title (verso blank) A2: HT with text (cap²) headed *'ALEXIS and MENALCAS.'* On C2ᵛ. *'FINIS.'*

CW] A2ᵛ *Men.* Wert B2ᵛ Let

*Type:* text (C2): 22 ll., 222(251) x 125 mm., 182R.

*Notes:* Page numbers are centered in parentheses. No RT. On title page 'S' in 'ALEXIS' is inverted. L. 13 on B2ᵛ reads "migdnight." In pamphlet binder. Purchased from Dobell's in 1956. Pforzheimer 207. Wing C5859.

PR3364 .M75 1695

## 33.  1709

A | LETTER | FROM | ITALY, | To the Right Honourable | *CHARLES*, Lord *Halifax.* ‖ By Mr. *Joſeph Addiſon.* 1701. ‖ Together with the | Mourning *MUSE* of *Alexis.* | A PASTORAL. | Lamenting the Death of our Late Gracious | QUEEN MARY. ‖ *By Mr.* Congreve. 1695. ‖ To which is added the | Deſpairing LOVER. ‖ *London:* Printed and Sold by *H. Hills,* in *Black-fryars,* | near the Water-ſide, 1709.

*Collation:* 8°. A⁸, 8 leaves, pp. *1–2* 3–16, A², A4 signed.

*Contents:* A1: title (verso blank) A2: ‖ ‖ 'A | LETTER | FROM | ITALY, | To the Right Honourable | *CHARLES*, Lord *Halifax.* ‖ *Salve magna parens frugum Saturnia tellus,* | *Magna virûm! tibires Antiquæ laudis & Artis* | *Aggredior, ſanctos auſus recludere fontes.* | [to the right] Virg. Geo. 2'. ‖ with text (cap²). A5: 'THE | *Mourning MUSE* | OF | ALEXIS, | A | PASTORAL. ‖ *Infandum Regina jubes renovare dolorem!* Virg.' ‖ with text (cap²). A8ᵛ: *'The Deſpairing LOVER.'* | [33 lines]

CW] A3 Immor- [That] A7 Lo, [Lo] A8 The [*The*]

*Type:* Congreve's text (A6): 34 ll., 151(164) x 90 mm., 81R.

*Notes:* Page numbers are centered in parentheses. No RT. In pamphlet binder. Case 251.

PR3304 .L4 1709

## *Love for Love.*  1695

## 34.  1695

LOVE for LOVE: | A | COMEDY. | Acted at the | THEATRE in *Little Lincolns-Inn Fields,* | BY | His Majeſty's Servants. ‖ Written by Mr. *CONGREVE.* ‖ *Nudus agris, nudus nummis paternis,* | *Inſanire parat certa ratione modoque.* Hor. || *LONDON:* | Printed for *Jacob Tonſon,* at the *Judge's-Head,* near the | *Inner-Temple-Gate* in *Fleetſtreet.* 1695.

*Half-title,* A1: || LOVE *for* LOVE. | Written by | Mr. *CONGREVE.* ||

*Collation:* 4°. A⁴ a⁴ B-M⁴ N², 54 leaves, pp. [*16*] 1–92 [misprinting 37 as 73], $2 [-N2] signed.

HT] ||| LOVE for LOVE. ||

*Contents:* A1: half-title (verso blank). A2: title (verso blank). A3: || || 'TO THE | RIGHT HONOURABLE | CHARLES | Earl of *Dorſet* and *Middleſex,* | *Lord Chamberlain of His Majeſty's Houſhold,* and *Knight* | of the *Moſt Noble Order of the Garter,* &c.' (cap³) signed on A4 'WILL. CONGREVE.' A4ᵛ: blank. a1: || || 'A | PROLOGUE | FOR | The opening of the new Play-Houſe, | propos'd to be ſpoken by Mrs. *Brace-* | *girdle* in Man's Cloaths. | Sent from an unknown Hand.' | [54 ll. '*C²USTOM, which every where bears mighty Sway,*']. On a2: [separated rules]. a2ᵛ: || || 'PROLOGUE. | Spoken at the opening of the New Houſe, | By Mr. *Betterton.*' | [47 ll. '*T²HE Husbandman in vain renews his Toil,*']. On a3: [rule]. a3ᵛ: || || 'EPILOGUE | Spoken at the opening of the New Houſe, | By Mrs. *Bracegirdle.*' [44 ll. '*S²URE Providence at firſt, deſign'd this Place*']. On a4: [rule] a4ᵛ: 'Perſonæ Dramatis.' (with cast). B1: HT with text (cap⁴) headed 'ACT I. SCENE I.' On N2ᵛ || '*FINIS.*' ||

CW] a4 Perſonæ B4ᵛ *Val.* C4ᵛ *Enter* D4ᵛ Sir E3 *Mrs Fore.* [Mrs. *Fore.*] F4ᵛ *Enter* G4ᵛ *Mrs. Fore.* H4ᵛ (Incli-) nation; I3ᵛ *Scan.* Ma- [*Scan.* Madam,] K4ᵛ means L4ᵛ his M2ᵛ *Mrs. Fore.* [Mrs. *Fore.*] N2 gene- [generally]

*Type:* text (C2): 38 ll., 177(194) x 118 mm., 93R.

*Notes:* No RT. Page numbers are centered in parentheses in the headline. Several page nos. cropped. N2 is lacking and has been supplied with a photostat from the Ashley Library copy. Bound in half calf with marbled boards. Purchased in Florence in 1949. W & M 236. Wing C5851. Pforzheimer 202.

PR3364 .L7 1695

## 35. 1695

[*title*] as in 1695 (34.) except for . . . Mr. *CONGREVE.* || The Second Edition. ||

*Collation:* 4°. A-M⁴, 48 leaves, pp. [*10*] 1–85 *86*, $2 signed.

HT] [as in 34. except for separated double rule]

*Contents:* A1: title (verso blank). A2: dedicatory epistle (cap³). A3: anonymous prologue (cap²). A4: prologue (cap²). B1: epilogue (cap²). B1ᵛ: dramatis personae (with cast). B2: HT with text (cap⁴).

CW] A4ᵛ EPILOGUE B4ᵛ Man C4ᵛ *Frail.* D4ᵛ *Fore.* E4ᵛ for F1 ACT. [ACT] G4ᵛ (Morn-) ing, -- H4ᵛ *Jere.* I1 *Weſt-* [*Weſtminſter-Hall:*] K4ᵛ *Ang.* L4ᵛ *Fore.* [CW torn off D1, K4; no CW on A2ᵛ]

*Type:* text (B3ᵛ): 40 ll., 185(197) x 118 mm., 92R.

Notes: No RT. Page numbers are centered in the headline in parentheses. Leaves A2, A3, M-M4 are lacking and have been supplied with photostats from the British Museum copy. The verso of M4 has not been reproduced. Bound in blue and gold ornamented boards. Purchased in Florence in 1949. W & M 233. Wing C5852. Pforzheimer 203.

PR3364 .L7 1695a

## 36. 1697

[*title*] as in 1695 (35.) except for ‖ The Third Edition. ‖ [5 lines] . . . 1697.

*Collation:* 4°. A-M⁴, 48 leaves, pp. [*10*] 1–85 *86*, $2 signed.

HT] [as in 35.]

*Contents:* A1: title (verso blank). A2: dedicatory epistle (cap³). A3: anonymous prologue (cap²). A4: prologue (cap²). B1: epilogue (cap²). B1ᵛ: dramatis personae (with cast). B2: HT with text (cap⁴) M4ᵛ: blank.

CW] A4ᵛ EPILOGUE B4ᵛ Man C4ᵛ *Frail.* D2ᵛ Tobacco- [Tobacco] E3ᵛ *Mrs.* [Mrs.] F1 ACT. [ACT] G4ᵛ (morn-) ing, — H4ᵛ *Jere.* I1 *Weſt-* [*Weſtminſter-Hall:*] K4ᵛ *Ang.* L4ᵛ *Fore.* [no CW on A2ᵛ]

*Type:* text (B3ᵛ): 40 ll., 186(196) x 119 mm., 93R.

*Notes:* Page numbers are centered in parentheses in the headline. Several page nos. cropped. No RT. Apparently a reprint of 35. partly by pages and partly by gatherings. Bound in blue and gold ornamented boards. Purchased in Florence in 1949. W & M 236. Wing C5854.

PR3364 .L7 1697

## 37. 1704

[*title*] as in 1697 (35.) except for *LOVE* for *LOVE.* | [3 lines] . . . *Little-Lincoln's-Inn-Fields,* | [8 lines] ‖ The FOURTH EDITION. ‖

*LONDON,* | Printed for *Jacob Tonʃon:* And Sold by *R. Wellinaton,* | *G. Strahan,* and *B. Lintott.* 1704.

*Collation:* 4°. A-L⁴, 44 leaves, pp. [*10*] 1–78, $2 signed.

HT] ‖ ‖ *LOVE* for *LOVE.* ‖

*Contents:* A1: title (verso blank). A2: dedicatory epistle (cap³). A3: anonymous prologue (cap²). A4: prologue (cap²). B1: epilogue (cap²). B1ᵛ: dramatis personae (with cast). B2: HT with text (cap³).

CW] A4ᵛ EPI- B4ᵛ *Trap.* C4ᵛ that D4ᵛ Sir E2ᵛ (Tar-) pawlin [pawlin---] F4ᵛ *Ben.* G4ᵛ Dreaming H4ᵛ (chit-) ty-fac'd I4 acknow- [acknowledge] K4ᵛ *Tatt.* [no CW on A2ᵛ]

*Type:* text (B3): 42 ll., 195(207) x 125 mm., 93R.

*Notes:* Page numbers are centered in the headline in brackets. No RT. Bound in blue cloth. Purchased in 1949.

PR3364 .L7 1704


## 38. 1735

[*title*] identical with *Love for Love* section title of 1735 edition of *Plays* except that opening line of title is not cropped.

*Notes:* A separate binding of the text of the single play from 1735 *Plays* (103.). Bound in blue cloth.

PR3364 .L7 1735


## 39. 1735

*LOVE* for *LOVE.* | A | COMEDY. ‖ [2-line motto from Horace and 1-line ack.] ‖ [orn. (18 x 30): floral basket] ‖ *DUBLIN:* Printed, by THEO. JONES, | For GEOGE ERISK, [stet] at *Shakeʃpear's* Head, GEORGE | EWING, at the Angel and Bible, and WILLIAM | SMITH at the *Hercules,* in *Dame-ʃtreet,* Bookʃellers, | M, DCC, XXXV.

*Collation:* 12°. A⁶ B-E¹², 54 leaves, pp. *1–8* 9–106 *107–108,* $5 (-A4.5, D3) signed.

HT] [orn. as on 1736 *Works* (113.), vol. 2, E7] | *LOVE* for *LOVE* ‖

*Contents:* A1: title (verso blank). A2: dedicatory epistle (fact⁵) headed by orn. [as on 113., vol. 2, E2]. A3ᵛ prologue (cap²) headed by orn. [scrollwork (4 x 71)].

on A4 orn. [as on 113., vol. 2, E6]. A4ᵛ: dramatis personae. A5: HT with text (fact⁷). on E11ᵛ orn. [as on 113., vol. 2, G3]. E12: epilogue (cap²) headed by orn. [flowers laced in triangles and ovals (6 x 70)]. on E12ᵛ orn. [as on 113., vol. 2, O8ᵛ].

RT] LOVE *for* LOVE. [LOVE B6ᵛ C7ᵛ]

CW] A4 DRA. [Dramatis] B12ᵛ he C1 (a-) abroad [broad] D12ᵛ *Frail.* E7ᵛ Mrs. *Fore.* [Mrs *Fore.*] E9 *Tat-* [*Tat.*] E11 Infidels [infidels,] [no CW on D3ᵛ, E2ᵛ]

*Type:* text (A6): 41 ll., 137(145) x 72 mm., 67R.

*Notes:* The text of the play in the 1736 Dublin *Works* (113.) is a resetting of this edition. Sewn with glued brown wrapper.

PR3364 .L7 1735a

## 40. 1756

[in black and red] LOVE *for* LOVE. | A | COMEDY. ‖ [2-line motto from Horace and ack.] ‖ Written by Mr. *CONGREVE.* ‖ [device: T1] ‖‖ LONDON: | Printed for J. and R. TONSON in the *Strand.* | [partial rule] | MDCCLVI.

*Collation:* 12°. A-D¹² E⁶, 54 leaves, pp. *1–11* 12–106 *107–108*, $5 (-E4.5) signed.

HT] [orn.: a modified T43]. LOVE *for* LOVE. ‖

*Contents:* A1: blank. A1ᵛ: engraving. A2: title (verso blank). A3: dedicatory epistle (fact⁵) headed by orn. (T81). A4ᵛ: prologue (cap²). On A5: triangle of fleuron type orn. A5ᵛ: dramatis personae (with cast). A6: HT with text (fact⁶). E6: epilogue (cap²). On E6ᵛ: triangle of fleuron type orn.

RT] LOVE *for* LOVE. [LOVE (no period) A6ᵛ; LOVE: C8, E4]

CW] A12ᵛ you B12ᵛ as C12ᵛ *Buck* [*Buckr.*] D12ᵛ laugh

*Type:* text (A12): 41 ll., 135(143) x 73 mm., 66R.

*Notes:* The engraving is the Hayman engraving of the 1753 *Works*. The engraved surface measures 121 x 74 mm., and is signed on the left '*F. Hayman delin*' and on the right '*G. V.ᵈʳ Gucht Sculp.*' Press figures are present as follows: A7ᵛ-1, A11-4, B12-4, B12ᵛ-3, C2ᵛ-2, C6-3, D6ᵛ-2, D8ᵛ-2, D12-4, E3ᵛ-2. Bound in green cloth.

PR3364 .L7 1756

## 41. 1757

LOVE for LOVE. | A | COMEDY. | BY | Mr. CONGREVE. | [two-line motto from Horace and ack.] | [orn. (20 x 33): similar to T42; bird faces left] | DUBLIN. | Printed for PETER WILSON, in *Dame-ſtreet.* | [partial rule] | M DCC LVII.

*Collation:* 12°. A-D¹², 48 leaves, pp. *1–5* 6–7 *8* 9–94 *95–96* $5 (-A2, C4) signed.

HT] [orn. as on 1736 *Works* (113.,) vol. 2, A7] | LOVE for LOVE. | [single row fleuron type orn.]

*Contents:* A1: title (verso blank). A2: prologue (cap²). A2ᵛ: dramatis personae (with cast). A3: HT with text (cap⁴). D12: epilogue (cap²) headed by orn. [illuminated face with foliage (8 x 70)]

RT] LOVE *for* LOVE. [LOVE (no period) C7ᵛ]

CW] A12ᵛ *Fore.* B12ᵛ I'll C12ᵛ *Jer.* D1ᵛ *Jer.* [*Fore.*]

*Type:* text (A4): 42 ll., 138(147) x 73 mm., 66R.

*Notes:* This edition does not follow the scene divisions of the Tonson *Works.* Acts divided by type orn. Bound in blue cloth.

PR3364 . L7 1757

## 42. 1760

[title] as in 1735 (39.) except for ‖ [orn. (as on 113., vol. 1, A1)] ‖ *DUBLIN:* | Printed for G. and A. EWING, W. SMITH, Sen. | J. EXSHAW, and H. BRADLEY, Bookſellers in | *Dame-ſtreet,* 1760.

*Collation:* 12°. A-B⁶ C-D¹² F⁶, 54 leaves, pp. *1–8* 9–106 *107–108.* $5 (-A4.5, B4.5, C4, F4.5) signed.

HT] [orn. as on 113., vol. 1, A2] | *LOVE* for *LOVE.* | [single flueron type orn.]

*Contents:* A1: title (verso blank). A2: dedicatory epistle (cap²) headed by orn. [flowers (8 x 69)]. A3ᵛ: prologue (cap²) headed by row of fleurons. A4ᵛ: dramatis personae. A5: HT with text (cap²). F6: epilogue (cap²) headed by row of fleurons. On F6ᵛ: orn. [imitation of T53].

RT] LOVE *for* LOVE.

CW] A6ᵛ *Val.* B6ᵛ *Tat.* C12ᵛ *Tat.* D4ᵛ (a-) bout [about] E12ᵛ and [no CW on E8ᵛ]

*Type:* text (A6): 41 ll., 136(144) x 73 mm., 67R.

*Notes:* This edition has been set from the text of the play of 1736 Dublin *Works* (113.). Acts divided by type orn. Bound in green cloth.

PR3364 . L7 1760

### 43.  1774

LOVE *for* LOVE. | A | COMEDY. | Written by | *Mr.* CONGREVE. ‖ [2-line motto from Horace and 1-line ack.] ‖ [triangle of fleurons] ‖ LONDON: | Printed for W. Fox, in *Holborn.* | [partial rule] | M DCC LXXIV.

*Collation:* 12°. B-E¹² F⁴, 52 leaves, pp. *1–9* 10–103 *104*, \$5 (-F3.4) signed.

HT] ‖| *LOVE* for *LOVE.* ‖

*Contents:* B1: title (verso blank). B2: dedicatory epistle (cap²) headed by double row of ivy type orn. B3: prologue (cap²) headed by row of garland type orn. On B3ᵛ: epilogue (cap²). B4ᵛ: dramatis personae (with cast). B5: HT with text (cap²). F4ᵛ: blank.

RT] LOVE *for* LOVE.

CW] B4ᵛ LOVE [*LOVE*] C6 *Jer* [*Jere.*] D12ᵛ This E12ᵛ Sir [no CW on E12]

*Type:* text (B7): 42 ll., 139(148) x 73 mm., 66R.

*Notes:* The play follows the scene division of the 1710 *Works.* Acts II and III, which do not begin a page, are separated from the preceding material by rules. No press figures. Bound in orange cloth.

PR3364 . L7 1774

### 44.  1774

Another copy.

*Notes:* This copy is preceded by a disjunct engraving headed '*ACT. V.* LOVE for LOVE. *Scene 9th.*' and below: '*Miss YOUNGE in the Character of*

*ANGELICA.* | *Had I the world to give you, it could not make* |*me worthy of so generous & faithful a Pa∫sion.*' The engraved surface, within a triple-ruled border, measures 118 x 82 mm., and is signed on the left '*Is. Roberts del. 1781.*' and on the right '*Roberts sc*'. The play is the third in a volume containing the other Congreve plays and Rowe's *Jane Shore* and *The Fair Penitent*. See items 17., 29., 65., and 86.

PR3362 . F6 1774

## 45. 1774

LOVE FOR LOVE. | A | COMEDY. | BY | WILLIAM CONGREVE. | [2-line motto from Horace and ack.] | EDINBURGH: | PRINTED AND SOLD BY J. ROBERTSON. | [partial rule] | M, DCC, LXXIV.

*Collation:* 12°. $\pi^2$ A-H$^6$, 50 leaves, pp. *i–iii* iv *v–vi 7* 8–99 *100*, plate (opp. sig. $\pi$1), $3 signed.

HT] LOVE FOR LOVE.

*Contents:* $\pi$1: title (verso blank). $\pi$2 dedicatory epistle (cap$^2$). A1: prologue. A1$^v$: dramatis personae. A2: HT with text (cap$^3$). H6$^v$: epilogue.

RT] LOVE for LOVE. [LOVE (no period) A2$^v$, B2, F3]

CW] A6$^v$ is B6 *Fore*, [*Fore.*] C6$^v$ ACT D4 *Sir San.* [*Sir Sam.*] E6$^v$ SCENE F6$^v$ been G6$^v$ a whole

*Type:* text (A3): 42 ll., 142(151) x 75 mm., 68R.

*Notes:* In the headline against the fold 'Act. I.' and according to act. Press figures are present as follows: A6$^v$-2, B6-2, C6$^v$-1, D6$^v$-2, E6$^v$-1, F6$^v$-2, G6$^v$-2, H6$^v$-2. The title is preceded by an apparently disjunct imitation of the Vander Gucht engraving (See 102.) in which Mrs. Frail casts her net for Ben. The engraved surface measures 122 x 75 mm. and is unsigned. The 2nd printed leaf is cropped at the bottom. The edition follows the scene divisions of the 1710 *Works*. In glued brown wrapper.

PR3364 . L7 1774a

## 46. 1784?

LOVE for LOVE. | A COMEDY. | WRITTEN BY | *Mr. CONGREVE.* | TAKEN FROM | THE MANAGER'S BOOK, | AT THE | Theatre Royal, Drury-Lane. ||| *LONDON:* | Printed by R. BUTTERS, No. 79, Fleet-∫treet; and ∫old by all the | Book∫ellers in Town and Country.

*Collation:* 12°. B⁴ C-F⁶ G², 30 leaves, pp. *1–4* 5–13 *14* 15–60 [57 mis-printed as 75 with the 7 inverted], plate (opp. sig. B1), $3 (-G2) signed.

HT] LOVE for LOVE. ‖

*Contents:* B1: title. B1ᵛ: dramatis personae (with cast). B2: HT with text (cap²).

RT] LOVE FOR LOVE. [LOVE (no period) E6; LOVE.] F3]

*Type:* text (C3): 50 ll., 148(155) x 77 mm., 59R.

*Notes:* There are no catchwords or press figures. Acts are separated by rules. The title is preceded by a disjunct unsigned engraving (100 x 58 mm.) of Mr. Ryder as Ben. Despite the claim that the cast listed with the dramatis personae is a CG cast, it is actually a DL cast, although it does not correspond exactly to the casts listed for any of the performances in the late 1770's or 1780's by Avery. The most similar is the performance of March 20, 1784 (Avery, p. 199) with the following differences: King as Valentine, Waldron as Trapland, Miss Tidswell as Mrs. Foresight, and Mrs. Jordan as Prue.

PR3364 . L7 1780

## 47. 1788

LOVE    FOR    LOVE. | A | COMEDY. | WRITTEN    BY | MR. CONGREVE. | Marked with the Variations in the | MANAGER's BOOK, | AT THE | 𝕿𝖍𝖊𝖆𝖙𝖗𝖊-𝕽𝖔𝖞𝖆𝖑 𝖎𝖓 𝕮𝖔𝖛𝖊𝖓𝖙-𝕲𝖆𝖗𝖉𝖊𝖓. ‖ *LONDON:* | Printed for W. LOWNDES; J. NICHOLLS; W. | NICOLL; S. BLADON; and J. BARKER. | MDCCLXXXVIII.

*Collation:* 12°. A² B-D¹² E¹⁰, 48 leaves, pp. *i–iii* iv–v *vi 1* 2–90, $6 (-E6) signed.

HT] LOVE FOR LOVE. ‖

*Contents: A1:* title. *A1ᵛ:* note of omissions. *A2:* prologue (cap²). On A2ᵛ: epilogue (cap²). B1ᵛ: dramatis personae (with casts) [printed vertically]. B2: HT with text (cap²).

RT] LOVE FOR LOVE.

CW] B1 DRA- [Dramatis] C12ᵛ *For.* D12ᵛ *Val.* [no CW on E6, E8ᵛ, E10]

*Type:* text (B4): 41 ll., 134(143) x 74 mm., 66R.

*Notes:* Press figures are present as follows: *A2*$^v$-3, B5$^v$-7, B7-3, C11-7, C11$^v$-7, D12-1, E10$^v$-1. Acts are headed by rules except III, which begins a page. This edition is a reprint of *LL* from the Lowndes 1788 *Works* (linear except for D1 and D2). The casts listed are the same except that Waldron as Foresight has been corrected to Parsons (Avery, p. 199).

PR3364 . L7 1788

## 48. 1791

*LOVE FOR LOVE.* | A | COMEDY. | [partial double rule] | *BY WILLIAM CONGREVE, ESQ.* | [partial double rule] | ADAPTED FOR | THEATRICAL REPRESENTATION | AS PERFORMED AT THE | *THEATRES-ROYAL DRURY-LANE AND COVENT-GARDEN.* | [partial double rule] | REGULATED FROM THE PROMPT-BOOKS, | *By Permission of the Managers.* ||| "The Lines distinguished by inverted Commas, are omitted in the Representation." ||| LONDON: | [partial double rule] | *Printed for the Proprietors, under the Direction of* JOHN BELL, | 𝔅𝔯𝔦𝔱𝔦𝔰𝔥 𝔏𝔦𝔟𝔯𝔞𝔯𝔶, STRAND, | Bookseller to His Royal Highness the Prince of Wales. | [partial rule] | M DCC XCI.

*Collation:* 4°. *A*² B-P⁴, 58 leaves, pp. *i–iv* v *vi* 7 8–114 *115–116*, plates [2] (opp. sig. *A*1), $1 signed.

HT] [orn. (19 x 71): comic mask with tambourine, horn, foliage] | LOVE FOR LOVE. |||

*Contents: A1:* title (verso blank). *A2:* introduction. *A2*$^v$: prologue. B1$^v$: dramatis personae (with casts). B2: HT with text. P4: epilogue. On P4$^v$ orn. [tambourine with foliage (17 x 30)].

RT] LOVE FOR LOVE.

*Type:* text (D1): 33 ll., 133(142) x 82 mm., 81R.

*Notes:* This edition has no catchwords or press figures. Acts are separated by double rules. In the headline against the fold '*Act I.*' and according to act. Lines numbered irregularly within right margin. The title page is preceded by two disjunct engravings. The first depicts Mr. Bannister, Jr. as Ben proposing to Prue (III, 7); the engraved surface measures 117 x 79 mm. and is signed on the left '*Ie Wilde ad viv. pinxt.*' and on the right '*Bromley sculp.*' At the bottom an imprint date of April 10, 1791. The second depicts the mad Valentine frightening Buckram (IV, 9); the engraved surface, within double rules, measures 124 x 76 mm. and is signed on the left '*Smirke pinxt.*' and on the right '*Neagle sculp.*' The imprint date below is May 20, 1791. The stubs of the remainder of these two leaves and the free end-paper appear between *A2* and *B1*. The stub of the back free end-paper appears between O4 and P1. The volume has been bound in brown boards. With the exception of Mrs. Hopkins as the nurse, the DL cast listed is that of the October 25, 1791 performance; the CG cast listed is that of the November 15, 1786 performance (Avery, p. 199).

PR3364 . L7 1791

## 49. 1791

Another copy.

*Notes:* The play is bound as the second in a volume containing additionally Cumberland's *Battle of Hastings*, Farquhar's *Recruiting Officer*, and Lee's *Rival Queens*. All are Bell editions with publication dates of 1792 or 1793. Each is paged and signed separately. The volume has no title, but the spine reads 'BRITISH | THEATRE' and below are printed the titles of the plays. A canceled stub precedes the *LL* title, and one comes between L1 and L2; these would seem to be plates of engravings, like those in 48., which have been excised. The Ben illustration, which bears an Act number, would be an appropriate frontispiece; the mad Valentine engraving would appropriately face L2.

PR1245 . B42 1791

## *A Pindarique Ode, Humbly Offered to the King, on His Taking Namur.* 1695

## 50. 1695

[within double rules] A | PINDARIQUE | ODE, | Humbly Offer'd to the | KING | On His Taking | NAMURE. || By Mr. *CONGREVE.* || *Præsenti tibi Maturos largimur Honores:* | *Nil oriturum aliàs, nil ortum tale fatentes.* | [to the right] Hor. ad Auguſtum. || *LONDON:* | Printed for *Jacob Tonſon* at the *Judge's-Head* | near the *Inner-Temple-Gate* in *Fleetſtret,* [sic] | M DC XCV.

*Collation:* 2°. *A²* B-C², 6 leaves, pp. [*2*] 1–6 9–11 *12* [ = 10] [misprinting '10' as '01'], $1 signed.

HT] || || A | PINDARIQUE | ODE.

*Contents: A1:* title (verso blank) *A2:* HT with text (cap²). On C²: || *'FINIS.'* || C2ᵛ: *'Books Printed for* Jacob Tonſon.'

CW] *A2*ᵛ Beings B2ᵛ Till

*Type:* text (B1): 23 ll., 213(234) x 134 mm., 180R.

*Notes:* Page numbers are centered in brackets. No RT. On the basis of the Tonson advertisement Pforzheimer 209 calls this a 2nd issue of the 1st edition. Unbound. The advertisement includes Congreve's "The Morning Muse of Alexis." Purchased in 1960 from Thorp's. Wing C5871.

PR3364 . P5 1695

# *Letters upon Several Occasions.* 1696

## 51. 1696

[within double rules] LETTERS | Upon ʃeveral | OCCASIONS: | Written by and between | [3 lines in double columns bᵣaced in the center to left and right] Mr. *Dryden,* Mr. *Congreve,* | Mr *Wycherly,* and | Mr. --------- Mr. *Dennis.* || Publiʃhed by Mr. DENNI·S. || With a New Tranʃlation of Select | LETTERS of *Monʃieur Voiture.* || *LONDON,* | Printed for *Sam. Briʃcoe,* at the Corner-Shop | of *Charles-Street* in *Ruʃʃel-Street* in *Covent* | *Garden.* 1696.

*Half-title*: K4: Select Letters | OF | VOITURE. || *The First, Tranʃlated* | *By Mr.* DRYDEN. | *And the reʃt* | *By Mr.* DENNIS. ||

*Collation:* 8°. A-I⁸ i⁸ K-N⁸, 112 leaves, pp. [16] 1–103 *104* 105–128 [16] 129–133 *134–135* 136–190 [2] [67 misnumbered as 76], \$4 (-D4, E3, I4) signed [misprinting F4 as F3].

*Contents:* A1: title (verso blank). A2: || || 'To the Right Honourable | *Charles Montague,* Eʃq;. | One of the Lords of the | Treaʃury, | Chancellor of | the Exchequer; and one | of His Majeʃties moʃt Ho- | nourable Privy Council.' (cap⁸) signed on A7ᵛ 'John Dennis.' A8: 'To the READER.' (cap²). B1: || 'A | COLLECTION | OF | LETTERS, | Written by ʃeveral Eminent Hands.' || (cap⁴). H5. || || 'LETTERS | OF | LOVE, | Written by ---------' (cap⁴). On I3ᵛ || 'The End of the Love Letters.' ||. K1: || || 'A Dedication deʃigned to | the Volunteers. | By Mrs.* Shadwell. | To the QUEEN. | *Written By Mr.* Dennis.' (cap²) K4 :Voiture half-title. K4ᵛ: letters (cap²). N8 || 'ERRATA.' N8ᵛ: || 'A Catalogue of Books Iately Printed | for *Samuel Briʃcoe,* at the Corner | of *Charles-ʃtreet, Covent-Garden.'* [5 items].

RT] LETTERS *on* | *ʃeveral Occaʃions* B1ᵛ-K3. [LEETERS *on* B4ᵛ, C4ᵛ, D1ᵛ, E1ᵛ, F3ᵛ, G4ᵛ, H2ᵛ, I2ᵛ, K2ᵛ: LETTERS *on* i6; *ʃeveral Occaʃions.* | LETTERS *on* i6ᵛ–i7.] Voiture'*s Letters.* K4ᵛ–N7ᵛ [Voiture's K8, L8, M7ᵛ–M8, N4, N7ᵛ; Volture's K7ᵛ, L7ᵛ]

CW] A2 pre- [Preſumption:] B6ᵛ *Copy* [*Mr.*] C7ᵛ *Copy* [*Mr.*] D3ᵛ *To* [*Mr.*] E5ᵛ *My* [*Written*] F5 Fault [fault] F5ᵛ Or, [or] H4 LET- [H4ᵛ blank] I6 Witty [very Witty] I8ᵛ *A* [*Mr.*] i8 *To* [*Mr.*] i8ᵛ A [*A*] K3 SELECT [K3ᵛ blank] L8ᵛ to M1 *To* [TO] M1ᵛ to [o (t not printing)] [no cw on B8ᵛ, D4ᵛ, I3ᵛ, i7].

*Type:* text (B3): 30 ll. 139(150) x 79 mm., 93 R.

*Notes:* The volume contains three letters of Congreve—110, 112, 115 in *William Congreve: Letters & Documents,* ed. John C. Hodges (New York and London, 1964). Bound in blue cloth. Wing D1033.

PN6131 . L4 1696

# *The Mourning Bride.* 1697

## 52. 1697

THE | Mourning Bride, | A | TRAGEDY. | As it is ACTED | AT THE | Theatre in *Lincoln's-Inn-Fields,* | BY | His Majeſty's Servants. || Written by Mr. *CONGREVE.* || —*Neque enim lex æquior ulla,* | *Quàm necis artifices arte perire ſua.* | [to the right] Ovid. de Arte Am. || *LONDON,* | Printed for *Jacob Tonſon* at the *Judge's Head* near the | *Inner-Temple-Gate,* in *Fleet-ſtreet,* 1697.

*Half-title:* π1: || THE | Mourning Bride, | A | TRAGEDY. ||

*Collation:* 4°. π² A-I⁴ K², 40 leaves, pp. [*12*] 1–56 65–74 *75–76* [=68], $2 [-K2] signed.

HT] || || THE | Mourning Bride. ||

*Contents:* π1: half title (verso blank). π2: title (verso blank). A1: || || 'TO | Her Royal Highneſs, | THE | PRINCESS.' (orn. initial⁴). Signed on A3 '*William Congreve.*' A3ᵛ: || || 'PROLOGUE. | Spoken by Mr. *Betterton.*' | [44 ll. '*T²HE Time has been when Plays were not ſo plenty,*']. A4ᵛ: 'Perſonae Dramatis.' (with cast). B1: HT with text (cap⁴) headed 'ACT I. SCENE I.' K2: || || 'EPILOGUE, | Spoken by Mrs. *Bracegirdle.*' | [31 ll. '*T²HE Tragedy thus done, I am, you know,*'].

RT] *The Mourning Bride.* [*Bride* (no period) C3, E3, G3, I3]

CW] A4ᵛ THE B1ᵛ To [Then] C4ᵛ *Alm.* [Sure,] D4ᵛ Our E1 Some-[Somewhat] F1 A Tor- [A Torture--] G3ᵛ Where-[Wherefore] H3 *Alonz.* [*Alon.*] I3ᵛ A Mar- [A Martyr] K1ᵛ EP- [EPILOGUE, ]

*Type:* text (B2): 38 ll. 179(192) x 115 mm., 96R.

*Notes:* Page numbers in headline against outer margin of type-page. The leaves have been pasted on larger cut-out leaves and the volume bound in brown cloth. The half-title ($\pi$1) and the epilogue (K2) are facsimile reproductions. W & M 237. Wing C5856. Pforzheimer 205. Stratman 1222.

PR3364 . M7 1697

## 53. 1697

[*title*] as in 1697 [52.] except for ‖ 𝔗𝔥𝔢 𝔖𝔢𝔠𝔬𝔫𝔡 𝔈𝔡𝔦𝔱𝔦𝔬𝔫. ‖ *LONDON,* | Printed for *Jacob Tonſon,* at the *Judge's-Head,* near the | *Inner-Temple-Gate,* in *Fleet-ſtreet.* 1697.

*Half-title:* $\pi$1: as in 1697 [52.]

*Collation:* 4°. $\pi^2$ A-I⁴ K², 40 leaves, pp. [*12*] 1–66 *67–68,* $2 (-K2) signed.

HT] as in 1697 [52.]

*Contents:* $\pi$1: half-title (verso blank). $\pi$2: title (verso blank). A1: dedicatory epistle (orn. initial⁴). A3ᵛ: prologue (cap²). A4ᵛ: dramatis personae (with cast). B1: HT with text (cap⁴). K2: epilogue (cap²).

RT] as in 1697 [52.] except for period on C3, E3, and G3.

CW] A4ᵛ THE B2 *Leo* [*Leo.*] B3ᵛ *En-* [*Enter*] C4ᵛ *Alm.* D4ᵛ Our E1 Some- [Somewhat] E3 Nightly: [Nightly;] F1 A Tor- [A Torture--] G3ᵛ Where- [Wherefore] H3 *Alonz.* [*Alon.*] I3ᵛ A Mar- [A Martyr] K1ᵛ EPI- [EPILOGUE,]

*Type:* text (B2): 38 ll., 178(193) x 117 mm., 94R.

*Notes:* Page numbers in headline against outer margin of type-page. Bound in brown boards, cloth reinforced. W & M 238. Wing C5858. Stratman 1223.

PR3364 . M7 1697a

## 54. 1697

[*title*] as in 1697 (53.) except for ‖ *LONDON,* | Printed for *JACOB TONSON,* at the *Judg's-Head,* near the | *Inner-Temple-Gate,* in *Fleet.ſtreet.* 1679.

*Half-title:* π1: as in 1697 (53).

*Collation:* 4°. π² A-I⁴ K², 40 leaves, pp. [*12*] 1–66 *67–68*, $2 (-K2) signed.

HT] as in 1697 (53.)

*Contents:* π1: half-title (verso blank). π2: title (verso blank) A1: dedicatory epistle (orn. initial⁴). A3ᵛ: prologue (cap²) A4ᵛ: dramatis personae (with cast). B1: HT with text (cap³). K2: epilogue (cap²).

RT] as in 1697 (53.) except for period on I3.

CW] A4ᵛ THE B3ᵛ *En-* [*Enter*] C4ᵛ *Alm.* D1 'Tis ['tis] D2ᵛ: What's [Whar's] E1 Some- [Somewhat] F1 A Tor- [A Torture--] G3ᵛ Where- [Wherefore] H3 *Alonz.* [*Alonz*] H4ᵛ *Scene* [*Scen*] I3ᵛ A Mar- [A Martyr] K1ᵛ EPI- [EPILOGUE,]

*Type:* text (B2): 38 ll., 175(188) x 116 mm., 92R.

*Notes:* Page numbers in headline against outer margin of type-page. The type setting of the edition notation on the title page is slightly smaller than in 53., and the period is not a black-letter period as in 53. This copy has the characteristics of a piracy noted of Pforzheimer 206. In brown wrapper. W & M 239. Wing C5857. Stratman 1225.

PR3364 . M7 1697b

## 55. 1697

Another copy.

*Notes:* Half-title lacking. The leaves have been cropped at the sides and the top and bottom. Bound in blue cloth.

PR3364 . M7 1697b cop.2

## 56. 1703

[*title*] as in 1697 (52.) except for THE | *MOURNING BRIDE.* | [13 lines] ‖ The THIRD EDITION. ‖ *LONDON,* | Printed for *Jacob Tonfon:* And Sold by *R. Wellington,* | *G. Strahan,* and *B. Lintott.* 1703.

*Half-title:* π1: ‖ THE | *MOURNING BRIDE.* | A | TRAGEDY. ‖

*Collation:* 4°. π² A-I⁴ K², 40 leaves, pp. [*12*] 1–66 *67–68*, $2 (-K2) signed.

HT] ‖ ‖ THE | *MOURNING BRIDE.* ‖

*Contents:* π1: half-title (verso blank). π2: title (verso blank) A1: dedicatory epistle (cap³). A3ᵛ: prologue (cap²). A4ᵛ: dramatis personae (with cast). B1: HT with text (cap⁴). K2: epilogue (cap²).

RT] as in 1697 (52.) except that there are no variants.

CW] A4ᵛ THE B4ᵛ Upon C3 ACT. [ACT] D4ᵛ Our E1 Some- [Somewhat] F4ᵛ From G3ᵛ Where- [Wherefore] H4ᵛ *Scene* I4ᵛ And

*Type:* text (B2): 38 ll., 178(191) x 121 mm., 94R.

*Notes:* Page numbers in headline against outer margin of type-page except for '1', in brackets centered in headline. Bound in blue cloth. Stratman 1226.

PR3364 . M7 1703

## 57. 1710

THE | MOURNING BRIDE. | A | TRAGEDY, | As it is now ACTED at the | THEATRE-ROYAL. ‖ Written by Mr. CONGREVE. ‖ [2-line motto from Ovid and 1-line ack.] ‖ [three squares of fleurons (12 x 12)] ‖ *LONDON:* Printed for *H. H.* in the Year 1710.

*Collation:* 4°. A-G⁴, 28 leaves, pp. *1–7* 8–56, $2 signed.

HT] ‖ ‖ THE | MOURNING BRIDE. ‖

*Contents:* A1: title (verso blank). A2: dedicatory epistle (cap³). A3: prologue (cap²). A3ᵛ: dramatis personae (with cast) A4: HT with text (cap⁶). On G4ᵛ: epilogue (cap²) [in double columns].

RT] *The* MOURNING BRIDE.

CW] A4ᵛ But B4ᵛ Now, C4ᵛ *Ofm.* O D2 Preceeds [*stet*] E4ᵛ *Zar.* And F4ᵛ O Fate G3ᵛ I under- [I underſtand]

*Type:* text (B1): 47 ll., 193(202) x 106 mm., 82R.

*Notes:* CW's are frequently printed on the last line of letter press. The edition follows the scene divisions of the 1710 *Works.* Acts which do not begin a page are headed by a rule. This edition repeats the "savage Beast" error of **54.** Stratman 1227.

PR3364 . M7 1710

## 58. 1733

[*title*] identical with *Mourning Bride* section title of 1733 *Dramatick Works* (102.)

*Notes:* A binding of the text of the play from the 1733 edition of the *Dramatick Works* with five other plays—Rowe's *The Royal Convert*, Lee's *Mithridates* and *Theodosius*, Rowe's *The Ambitious Stepmother*, and the anonymous *The Fair Circassian*—each with its own title page and each signed and paged separately. The imprint dates vary from 1732 to 1735. There is no volume title. The spine bears the title 'PLAYS.'

PR1245 . P5 1733

## 59. 1742

[in black and red] THE | MOURNING BRIDE. | A | TRAGEDY. | Written by *Mr.* CONGREVE. ‖ [2-line motto from Ovid and 1-line ack.] ‖ [device: T1] ‖‖ *LONDON:* | Printed for J. and R. TONSON in the *Strand.* | [short rule] | M DCC XLII.

*Collation:* 12°. A-C¹², 36 leaves, pp. *1–11* 12–71 *72*, $5 (-A4) signed.

HT] [orn. (T8)] | THE | MOURNING BRIDE. ‖

*Contents:* A1: blank. A1ᵛ: engraving. A2: title (verso blank). A3: dedicatory epistle (fact⁶) headed by orn. (T3). A4ᵛ: prologue (cap²). A5ᵛ: dramatis personae (with cast). A6: HT with text (orn. initial⁵). On C12: orn. (T9). C12ᵛ: epilogue (cap²).

RT] *The* MOURNING BRIDE.

CW] A11ᵛ Now B12ᵛ Who, C1ᵛ Wor-[Worthy]

*Type:* text (A7): 41 ll., 134(143) x 71mm., 66R.

*Notes:* Press figure: B11ᵛ-7. The engraved illustration (A1ᵛ) depicts the scene (II, vi) in which Osmyn, ascending from the tomb, confronts Almeria and Leonora and is signed '*G. V:dr Gucht Inv. et Sculp.*' The engraved surface measures 131 x 74 mm. The ornament preceding the head title is similar to Richardson's 7 and 8 (Sale, p. 270) except that the cornucopias are at the ends of the ornament rather than near the bird. Small ornaments separate the acts. Scene divisions as in 1710 *Works.* Bound in blue cloth. Stratman 1237.

PR3364 . M7 1742

## 60. 1753

[in black and red]

[*title*] as in 1742 ed. (59.) except | Printed for J. and R. TONSON and S. DRAPER | in the *Strand*. | [partial rule] | M̲ DCC̲ LIII.

*Collation:* 12°. A-C¹², 36 leaves, pp. *1–11* 12–71 *72*, $5 (-A4) signed.

HT] [orn.: T84] | THE | MOURNING BRIDE. ||

*Contents:* A1: blank. A1ᵛ: engraving. A2: title (verso blank). A3: dedicatory epistle (fact⁵) headed by orn. (T85). A4ᵛ: prologue (cap²). A5ᵛ: dramatis personae (with cast). A6: HT with text (orn. initial⁵). On C12: orn. (T75). C12ᵛ: epilogue (cap²).

RT] *The* MOURNING BRIDE.

CW] A11ᵛ Now, B11 Ye [Yet] C1ᵛ Worthy

*Type:* text (A8): 41 ll., 134(142) x 73 mm., 65R.

*Notes:* No press figures. The acts are separated by a small orn. The engraving is the Vander Gucht engraving used in 59., 103., and 102. The edition is a linear reprint of the 1742 edition (59.). Bound in orange cloth. Not listed by Stratman.

PR3364 . M7 1753

## 61. 1757

THE | MOURNING BRIDE. | A | TRAGEDY. || [2-line motto from Ovid and 1-line ack.] || Written by Mr. WILLIAM CONGREVE. || [orn. (imitation of T57)] ||| DUBLIN: | Printed for PETER WILSON, in *Dame-ſtreet*. | [partial rule] | M DCC LVII.

*Collation:* 12°. A-C¹², 36 leaves, pp. *1–9* 10–71 *72*, $5 (-A3) signed.

HT] [orn. (28 x 67): woman receiving suppliants, cornucopias at sides, within border] | THE | MOURNING BRIDE. | [row of fleurons]

*Contents:* A1: title (verso blank). A2: dedicatory epistle (cap⁴) headed by orn. [as on 1736 *Works* (113.), vol. 2, A7]. A3ᵛ: prologue (cap²). A4ᵛ: dramatis personae. A5: HT with text (fact⁶). C12ᵛ: epilogue (cap²).

RT] *The* MOURNING BRIDE.

CW] A12ᵛ O ecſtaſie B8 Or, [Or]

*Type:* text (A6): 41 ll., 135(143) x 73mm., 65R.

*Notes:* No press figures. Scene divisions as in 1710 *Works.* Acts are headed by a single row of type orn., except for V, which begins a page. Bound in blue cloth. Stratman 1246.

PR3364 . M7 1757

## 62. 1763

[in black and red]

[*title*] as in 1753 (60.) except | Mr. CONGREVE. | [2-line motto from Ovid and 1-line ack.] ||| LONDON: | Printed for J. and R. TONSON. | [partial rule] | M.DCC.LXIII:

*Collation:* 12°. A-C¹², 36 leaves, *1–11* 12–51 *52* 53–71 *72*, $5 signed.

HT] ||| ||| THE | MOURNING BRIDE. ||

*Contents:* A1: blank. A1ᵛ: engraving. A2: title (verso blank). A3: dedicatory epistle (cap²) headed by two double rules. A4ᵛ: prologue (cap²) headed by double rule. A5ᵛ: dramatis personae (with cast). A6: HT with text (cap²). C12ᵛ: epilogue (cap²) headed by double rule.

RT] *The* MOURNING BRIDE.

CW] A11ᵛ Now B3ᵛ SCENE. [SCENE] B12ᵛ Who, C1ᵛ Worthy C7 SCENE. [SCENE]

*Type:* text (A8): 41 ll., 138(145) x 74 mm., 67R.

*Notes:* No press figures. The acts are separated by double rules. The engraving is the Vander Gucht engraving. After p. 17, a linear reprint of the 1742 edition (59.). This edition is bound as the 4th play in a volume of 5 plays, each signed and paged separately, with the following title [in black and red]: 'THE | ENGLISH THEATRE. | IN | EIGHT VOLUMES. | CONTAINING | The moſt valuable PLAYS | Which have been acted on the | LONDON STAGE. || VOL. VI. || HENRY the FIFTH. | JANE SHORE. | KING LEAR. | MOURNING BRIDE. | ORPHAN. || LONDON: | Printed for T. LOWNDS in Fleet-ſtreet. | M DCC LXII. | Where may be had, All Sorts of PLAYS.' Stratman C86.

PR3364 . M7 1763

## 63. 1764

THE | MOURNING BRIDE. | A | TRAGEDY. | Written by | Mr. CONGREVE. | [2-line motto from Ovid and 1-line ack.] ||| LONDON: | Printed for J. and R. TONSOM. | [partial rule] | M DCC LXIV.

*Collation:* 12°. A⁵ B-F⁶, 35 leaves, pp. *3–11* 12–71 *72* [=70], $3 (-A3) signed.

HT] ||| ||| THE | MOURNING BRIDE. |

*Contents:* A1: title (verso blank). A2: dedicatory epistle (cap²) headed by double rule. A3ᵛ: prologue (cap²) headed by double rule. A4ᵛ: dramatis personae (with cast). A5: HT with text (cap²). F6ᵛ: epilogue (cap²) headed by double rule.

RT] *The* MOURNING BRIDE. [BRIDE, C2; BRIDE (no period) D1, D1ᵛ]

CW] A5ᵛ Is B5ᵛ Now C3ᵛ SCENE.[SCENE] C4ᵛ *Zara.* [*Zara,*] C6ᵛ *Hel* [*Heli.*] D6ᵛ Who E1ᵛ Worthy F1 SCENE.[SCENE] [no CW on B3ᵛ]

*Type:* text (B2): 41 ll., 137(145) x 73 mm., 67R.

*Notes:* No press figures. The acts are separated by double rules. The edition is a linear reprint of the 1763 (62.) edition. The misspelling of Tonson on the title page and the missing leaf in the first gathering (but with the second leaf signed 'A2'), which would normally be filled by the engraving, suggests that the edition is a forgery. Bound in blue cloth. Not listed in Stratman.

PR3364 . M7 1764

## 64. 1766

[in black and red]
[*title*] as in 1763 (62.) except for | M.DCC.LXVI.

*Collation:* 12°. A-C¹², 36 leaves, pp. *1–11* 12–71 *72*, $5 (+B6) signed.

HT] as in 1763 (62.)

*Contents:* as in 1763 (62.)

RT] *The* MOURNING BRIDE. [BRIDE (no period) B2, C4, C10]

CW] A11$^v$ Now B12$^v$ Who, C1$^v$ Worthy

*Type:* text (A8): 41 ll., 138(146) x 79 mm., 67R.

*Notes:* No press figures. A linear reprint of 1763 (62.). The Vander Gucht engraving has been replaced by the Hayman-Grignion engraving of Osmyn ascending from the tomb. See 1753 *Works* (115.). Bound in orange cloth. Stratman 1250.

PR3364 . M7 1766

## 65. 1774

THE | MOURNING BRIDE. | A | TRAGEDY. | Written by | *Mr.* CONGREVE. ‖ [2-line motto from Ovid and 1-line ack.] ‖ [triangle of fleurons] ‖‖ LONDON: | Printed for W. Fox, in *Holborn.* | [partial rule] | M DCC LXXIV.

*Collation:* 12°. B-C$^{12}$ D$^{10}$, 34 leaves, pp. *1–9* 10–67 *68*, plate (opp. sig. B1), $5 (-B3) signed.

HT] ‖‖ THE | *MOURNING BRIDE.* ‖

*Contents:* B1: title (verso blank). B2: dedicatory epistle (cap$^2$) headed by double row of type orn. [vine]. B3$^v$: prologue (cap$^2$) headed by double row of type orn. [garland]. B4$^v$: dramatis personae (with cast). B5: HT with text (cap$^3$). D10$^v$: epilogue (cap$^2$) headed by row of type orn. [ornamented X's].

RT] *The* MOURNING BRIDE.

CW] B12$^v$ *Ofm.* C12$^v$ The

*Type:* text (B7): 42 ll., 140(147) x 74 mm., 66R.

*Notes:* No press figures. Scene divisions as in 1710 *Works.* Acts III and IV, which do not begin a page, are headed by a rule. The disjunct engraving preceding the title depicts Mrs. Crawford as Almeria when she perceives the headless body of a man she believes to be Alphonso (V, 11). The engraved surface, within triple rules, measures 119 x 83 mm., and is signed on the left '*I. Roberts del. 1781.*' and on the right '*Is. Roberts sculp.*' The play is the fourth in a volume containing the five Congreve plays and Rowe's *Jane Shore* and *The Fair Penitent.* Stratman 1254.

PR3362 . F6 1774

## 66. 1774

[*title*] as in 65.

*Collation:* 12°. B¹ χ² B²-B¹² C¹² D¹⁰, 36 leaves, pp. *1–2* i–iv *3–9* 10–67 *68*, plate (opp. sig. B1), $5 (-B3) signed.

*Notes:* This copy is a separate binding of 65. Bound between the title and the dedicatory epistle is a 4-page life of Congreve, which in the volume of plays is bound between the title and dedicatory epistle of *The Old Bachelor* (17). Bound in blue cloth.

PR3364 .M7 1774

## 67. 1775

THE | MOURNING BRIDE, | A | TRAGEDY. | As it is Acted at the | THEATRES-ROYAL | IN | DRURY-LANE | AND | COVENT-GARDEN. ‖ Written by Mr. CONGREVE. ‖ [2-line motto from Ovid and 1-line ack.] ‖ [device: imitation of T1] ‖‖ LONDON: | Printed and Sold by W. OXLADE, at *Shakeſpeare's | Head*, [No. 35,] in George-Street, Old-Bailey. | M, DCC, LXXV.

*Collation:* 12°. A³ B–E⁶ F², 29 leaves, *1–7* 8–58, $3 (-F2) signed.

HT [row of type orn.] | THE | MOURNING BRIDE. ‖

*Contents: A1:* blank. *A1ᵛ:* engraving. *A2:* title. *A2ᵛ:* prologue (cap²). *A3:* epilogue (cap²). *A3ᵛ:* dramatis personae. B1: HT with text (cap²).

RT] *The* MOURNING BRIDE.

CW] B6ᵛ Exerts C6ᵛ *Zara.* [*Za.*] D6ᵛ Affection E6ᵛ *Zara.* [*Za.*] [CW cropped on B3, B3ᵛ, B4]

*Type:* text (C2): 46 ll., 136(143) x 64 mm., 59R.

*Notes:* No press figures. Scene divisions as in 1710 *Works.* Acts II and IV are headed by a row of type ornaments, Act III by a rule. The unsigned engraving is a reversed copy of the Hayman-Grignion engraving. The engraved surface measures 113 x 63 mm. Bound in blue cloth. Stratman 1255.

PR3364 .M7 1775

## 68.  1776

THE | *MOURNING BRIDE.* | A | TRAGEDY, | WRITTEN BY | MR. CONGREVE. | Marked with the Variations in the | MANAGERS BOOKS, | AT THE | 𝕿𝖍𝖊𝖆𝖙𝖗𝖊=𝕽𝖔𝖞𝖆𝖑 𝖎𝖓 𝕯𝖗𝖚𝖗𝖞=𝕷𝖆𝖓𝖊. | [2-line motto from Ovid and 1-line ack.] | [triangle of stars and ornamented X's] | *LONDON:* | PRINTED FOR T. LOWNDES, T. CASLON, | S. BLADON, and W. NICOLL. | M.DCC.LXXVI.

*Collation:* 12°. A–C¹², 36 leaves, pp. *i–iii* iv–v *vi* vii *viii 9* 10–67 *68* [4], plate (opp. sig. A1), $6 signed.

HT] THE | *MOURNING BRIDE.* ||

*Contents:* A1: title. A1ᵛ: omissions note. A2: dedicatory epistle (cap²). A3ᵛ: prologue (cap²). A4ᵛ: dramatis personae (with cast) [printed vertically]. A5: HT with text (cap²). C10ᵛ: epilogue (cap²). C11: 'PLAYS *printed for the* PROPRIETORS *of the* | *Copies, at* One Shilling *and* Sixpence *each.*' On C12: 'BOOKS *printed for* T. LOWNDES.'

RT] THE MOURNING BRIDE. [BRIDE (no period) A6]

CW] A12ᵛ His B1 Affliction ['Affliction] [no CW on B4ᵛ, C3, C11, C11ᵛ, C12]

*Type:* text (A6): 40 ll., 133(140) x 79 mm., 66R.

*Notes:* Press figures are present as follows: A5ᵛ-9, A11-6, B1ᵛ-6, B11-5, C1ᵛ-2, C2ᵛ-9. Acts II, IV, and V are headed by rules. The disjunct engraving preceding the title page is the Taylor-Walker engraving of Garrick as Osmyn ascending from the tomb (described more fully in 119.). This copy of the engraving does bear an imprint date, September 28, 1776. The DL cast listed is the cast listed for the November 21, 1775 performance (Avery, p. 206), except for Reddish as Osmyn and Whitfield as Heli. Bound in orange cloth. Not listed in Stratman.

PR3364 .M7 1776

## 69.  1777

THE | MOURNING BRIDE. | A | TRAGEDY. | As it is Acted at the | THEATRES-ROYAL | IN | Drury-Lane and Covent-Garden. || By Mr. CONGREVE. || [2-line motto from Ovid and ack.] || [orn. (26 x 32): pattern composed of fleurons] ||| LONDON: | Printed for J. WENMAN, No 144, FLEET-STREET; and Sold by all | other Bookſellers in Town and Country. | M DCC LXXVII.

*Collation:* 4°. A–B⁴, 8 leaves, pp. *1–3* 4–16, plate (opp. sig. A1), $2 signed.

HT] [orn. (16 x 115): rectangle of oval and diamond type orn. enclosing double line of type orn.] | THE | MOURNING BRIDE. [partial rule]

*Contents:* A1: title. A1ᵛ: [row of type orn.] prologue (cap²). On A1ᵛ: epilogue (cap²), dramatis personae. A2: HT with text (cap²).

RT] THE MOURNING BRIDE.

*Type:* text (B1): 2 cols., 73 ll., 199(206) x 115 mm.; printer's measure 56 mm., 54R.

*Notes:* The title page is preceded by a disjunct illustration of Mrs. Yates as Almeria kneeling to the King. The unsigned engraving, which is dated November 1, 1777, measures 113 x 87. No press figures or CW. The acts are separated by a row of type ornaments. A cancel stub is present between A4 and B1. Glued in a cardboard cover. Stratman 1257.

PR3364 .M7 1777

## 70. 1783

[*title*] as in 1776 (68.) except for | PRINTED FOR T. AND W. LOWNDES, S. BLADON, | AND W. NICOLL. | M. DCC. LXXXIII.

*Collation:* 12°. A–C¹²; 36 leaves, pp. *i–iii* iv–v *vi* vii *viii 9* 10–67 *68* [4], $6 signed.

HT] as in 1776 (68.)

*Contents:* as in 1776 (68.) except that both DL and CG casts are listed.

RT] THE MOURNING BRIDE. [BRIDE (no period) B12]

CW] A12ᵛ His B1 Affliction ['Affliction] [no CW on A2ᵛ, B4ᵛ, C11, C11ᵛ, C12]

*Type:* text (A6): 40 ll., 133(140) x 77 mm., 67R.

*Notes:* No press figures. A linear reprint of the 1776 edition (68.). The frontispiece and the front free end-paper are lacking. The DL cast is that of the March 18, 1783 performance; the CG cast is that of the December 2, 1782 performance except for M. Davies as Heli (Avery, p. 206). Stratman 1258.

PR3364 .M7 1783

## 71. 1787

THE | MOURNING BRIDE, | A | TRAGEDY, | WRITTEN | By Mr. CONGREVE. | MARKED | As performed at the Theatres-Royal | IN | DRURY-LANE | AND | COVENT-GARDEN. | [partial rule] | [2-line motto from Ovid and 1-line ack.] | [partial rule] | LONDON: | Printed and Sold by H. WHITWORTH, No. 3, | PLAYHOUSE-YARD, BLACK-FRIARS: Where Letter- | Preſs and Copper-Plate Printing are carried on with| the utmoſt Diſpatch, and on the moſt reaſonable Terms.

*Collation:* 12°. A–E⁶; 30 leaves, pp. *1–4* 5–59 *60*, plate (opp. sig. A1), $3 (-A2) signed.

HT] THE | *MOURNING BRIDE.* ||

*Contents:* A1: title. A1ᵛ: dramatis personae (with casts) [printed vertically]. A2: prologue (cap²). A2ᵛ: HT with text (cap²). E6ᵛ: epilogue (cap²).

RT] THE MOURNING BRIDE.

CW] A6ᵛ *King.* B6ᵛ *Ofm.* C4ᵛ Thus ['Thus] D3ᵛ She [But] E4 came [I came]

*Type:* text (A4): 42 ll., 138(146) x 72 mm., 66R.

*Notes:* The title page is preceded by a disjunct, unsigned engraving of Almeria preparing to kiss the dead man whom she believes to be Alphonso (V, xi). The engraved surface measures 121 x 83 mm. Acts II, IV, and V are headed by a rule. The DL cast listed is that of the May 19, 1787 performance; the CG cast that of the October 30, 1786 performance (Avery, pp. 206–7). These casts would suggest a 1787 date for the edition. Omitted passages are placed in single quotation marks. The copy, bound in blue cloth, has one unconjugate prefixed and concluding leaf, presumably binders' leaves. No press figures. Stratman 1264.

PR3364 .M7 1787

## 72. 1788

THE | MOURNING BRIDE. | A | TRAGEDY. | WRITTEN BY | MR. CONGREVE. | Marked with the Variations in the | MANAGER's BOOK, | AT THE | Theatre-Royal in Drury-Lane. || *LONDON:* | Printed for W. LOWNDES; J. NICHOLLS; W. | NICOLL; S. BLADON; and J. BARKER. | M DCC LXXXVIII.

*Collation:* 12°. a⁴ A–B¹² C⁶, 34 leaves, pp. *i–ii* iii–vii *viii 1* 2–59 *60*, plate (opp. sig. a1), $6 (-a3.4, C4.5.6) signed.

HT] THE | MOURNING BRIDE. ||

*Contents:* a1: title. a1ᵛ: omissions note. a2: dedicatory epistle (cap²). a3ᵛ: prologue (cap²). a4ᵛ: dramatis personae (with casts) [printed vertically]. A1: HT with text (cap²). C6ᵛ: epilogue (cap²).

RT] THE MOURNING BRIDE.

CW] a4 DRAMATIS [Dramatis] A11 *Ofm.* ['*Ofm.*] B1 *Heli.* [Is] C3ᵛ 'Or, ['Or]

*Type:* text (A3): 40 ll., 131(139) x 73 mm., 65R.

*Notes:* Press figures are present as follows: A11-4, A11ᵛ-6, B8ᵛ-3, B11ᵛ-2, C1ᵛ-4. Each act is headed by a rule. The title is preceded by the disjunct Taylor-Walker engraving of Garrick as Osmyn. The DL cast listed is that of the May 19, 1787 performance; the CG cast is that of the October 30, 1786 performance. Bound in red cloth. Stratman 1261.

PR3364 .M7 1788

## 73. 1791

THE | *MOURNING BRIDE.* | [partial double rule] | A | TRAGEDY. | [partial double rule] | *BY MR. CONGREVE.* | [partial double rule.] | ADAPTED     FOR | THEATRICAL     REPRESENTATION, | AS PERFORMED   AT   THE | THEATRES-ROYAL, | *DRURY-LANE AND   COVENT-GARDEN.* | [partial  double  rule]  REGULATED FROM  THE  PROMPT-BOOKS, | *By Permission of the Managers.* ||| "The  Lines  distinguished  by  inverted  Commas,  are  omitted  in  the Representation." ||| LONDON: | [partial double rule] | *Printed for the Proprietors,  under  the  Direction  of*  JOHN  BELL, | 𝕭𝖗𝖎𝖙𝖎𝖘𝖍 𝕷𝖎𝖇𝖗𝖆𝖗𝖞, STRAND, | Bookseller to his Royal Highness the Prince of Wales. | [partial rule] M DCC XCI.

*Collation:* 4°. *A*⁴ B–L⁴, 44 leaves, pp. *i–iii* iv–v *vi* vii–viii *9* 10 *11–13* 14–84 *85* 86 [2], $1 signed.

HT] [orn.: sword, wand, and manacles within a crown (15 x 51)] | THE MOURNING BRIDE. |||

*Contents: A1:* title (verso blank). *A2:* dedicatory epistle (title within double rules). *A3ᵛ:* introduction (title within double rules). *B1:* prologue (title within double rules). *B2:* blank. *B2ᵛ:* dramatis personae (with casts) [title within

double rules]. B3: HT with text. On L2ᵛ: orn. [Medusa-like head (20 x 21)].
L3: epilogue (title within double rules) L4ʳ⁻ᵛ: blank.

RT] THE MOURNING BRIDE.

*Type:* text (C1): 33 ll., 134(142) x 82 mm., 81R.

*Notes:* No press figures or CW. In the headline next fold '*Act I.*' and according to act in italic. Acts are separated by double rules. The lines are numbered by twenties within the right margin. The play was probably preceded by
a disjunct engraving, of which only the stub remains. The DL cast listed is that
of the January 6, 1789 performance; the CG cast that of the March 10, 1788
performance except for Mr. Powell as Garcia (Avery, p. 207). The play is the
last play in a volume containing additionally Cumberland's *The Brothers,* Cib-
ber's *The Careless Husband,* and Addison's *The Drummer.* The volume has no
title, but the spine is marked 'BRITISH | THEATRE' and below, the titles
of the plays. Not listed in Stratman.

PR3364 .M7 1791

## 74. 1791

[title] as in 1791 (73.) except for ... *BRIDE.* | [3 lines] BY MR.
CONGREVE. | [2 lines] *THEATRICAL REPRESENTATION,* |
[1 line] THEATRES-ROYAL | DRURY-LANE AND
COVENT-GARDEN. | [8 lines] ... *Direction of* | JOHN BELL,
𝔅𝔯𝔦𝔱𝔦𝔰𝔥=𝔏𝔦𝔟𝔯𝔞𝔯𝔶, STRAND, | ... PRINCE OF WALES.

*Collation:* 12°. A–H⁶, 48 leaves, pp. *i–iii* iv–v *vi* vii–viii *ix* x *xi–xii 13*
14–96, $3 signed.

HT] [orn. as in 73.] | THE | *MOURNING BRIDE.* |||

*Contents:* A1: title (verso blank). A2: dedicatory epistle (title within double
rules). A3ᵛ: introduction (title within double rules). A5: prologue (title within
double rules). A6: blank. A6ᵛ: dramatis personae (with casts) [title within
double rules]. B1: HT with text. On H6: epilogue. On H6ᵛ: orn. [as on L2ᵛ,
1791 (73.)].

RT] THE MOURNING BRIDE.

*Type:* text (B3): 30 ll., 112(119) x 68 mm., 75R.

*Notes:* Press figures are present as follows: C3ᵛ-1, D6-2, E4-2, E4ᵛ-1, H3ᵛ-2.
No CW. In the headline next fold '*Act I.*' and according to act in italic. Acts are

separated by double rules and scenes by single rules. The lines of each act are numbered, largely by twenties, within the right margin. The casts listed are those of 73. Glued in gray cloth cover. Stratman 1262.

PR3364 .M7 1791a

## The Birth of the Muse. 1698

### 75. 1698

THE | BIRTH | OF THE | MUSE. | A | POEM. | TO THE | RIGHT HONOURABLE | *CHARLES MONTAGUE,* | CHANCELLOUR | OF THE | EXCHEQUER, &c. ‖ By Mr. *CONGREVE.* ‖ *Dignum laude virum Muſa vetat mori.* Horat. ‖ *LONDON,* | Printed for *Jacob Tonſon* at the *Judge's Head* near the | *Inner-Temple-*Gate, in *Fleetſtreet.* 1698.

*Collation:* 2°. A–C², 6 leaves, pp. [*2*], 1–10, A², B1, C1 signed.

HT] ‖ ‖ THE | BIRTH | OF THE | MUSE.

*Contents:* A1: title (verso blank) A2: HT with text (cap³) On C2ᵛ: *'FINIS.'*

CW] A2ᵛ Nor [Not] B2 *Britania* [*sic*]

*Type:* B2ᵛ: 30 ll., 232(257) x 125 mm., 156R.

*Notes:* Page numbers are centered in brackets. No RT. Wing C5845. Pforzheimer 193.

PR3364 .B5 1698

## Amendments of Mr. Collier's False and Imperfect Citations. 1698

### 76. 1698

[within double rules] AMENDMENTS | OF | *Mr.* COLLIER's | *Falſe and Imperfect CITATIONS,* &c. | From the [play titles braced to left] OLD BATCHELOUR, | DOUBLE DEALER, | LOVE for LOVE, | MOURNING BRIDE. ‖ 𝕭𝖞 𝖙𝖍𝖊 𝕬𝖚𝖙𝖍𝖔𝖗 𝖔𝖋 𝖙𝖍𝖔𝖘𝖊 𝕻𝖑𝖆𝖞𝖘. ‖ *Quem recitas meus eſt o Fidentine Libellus,* | *Sed male dum recitas incipit eſſe tuus.* | [to the right] Mart. | *Graviter, & iniquo animo, maledicta tua pate-* | *rer, ſi te ſcirem Judicio magis, quem morbo animi,* | *petulantia iſta uti.* *Sed, quoniam in te neque mo-* | *dum, neque modeſtiam ullam animadverto, refpon-* | *debo tibi: uti, fi quam maledicendo voluptatem* | *cepifti, eam male-audiendo amittas.* | [to the right] Saluſt. Decl. || *LONDON,* | Printed for *J. Tonfon* at the *Judge*'s *Head* in *Fleet-ftreet,* | near the *Inner-Temple-Gate.* 1698.

*Half-title: A1*: || AMENDMENTS | OF | *Mr.* COLLIER'*s* | *Falfe and Imperfect CITATIONS,* &c. ||

*Collation:* 8°. *A*² B–H⁸ I⁴, 62 leaves, pp. [4] 1–80 71–109 *110* [=120], \$4 (-I3.4) signed.

HT] || || AMENDMENTS | OF | *Mr.* COLLIER'*s* | *Falfe and Imperfect CITATIONS,* &c.

*Contents:* A1: half-title (verso blank). A2: title. A2ᵛ: || 'ERRATA.' || B1: HT with text (cap³). On I4: '*FINIS.*' (verso blank).

CW] B6ᵛ con- [concluding] C6ᵛI [- -*I*] D1ᵛ Bellow- [Bellowing] E1 Whic [Which] F5 Say- ['Sayings] G7 gra- [gravell'd] H8ᵛ (Ex=) preſſions, [preſſions.]

*Type:* text (B3ᵛ): 24 ll. with mrg. nn., 140(152) x 76(91) mm., 117R.

*Notes:* No RT. Page numbers are centered in parentheses. According to *Pforzheimer Library* the first issue of the first edition. Bound in brown leather. The half-title bears the name of Samuell Sandys, the first Baron Sandys. Wing C5844. Pforzheimer 191. *Congreve* 99.

PN2047 .C62

## The Way of the World. 1700

## 77. 1700

THE | Way of the World, | A | COMEDY. | As it is ACTED | AT THE | Theatre in *Lincoln's-Inn-Fields,* | BY | His Majeſty's Servants. || Written by Mr. *CONGREVE.* || *Audire eſt Operæ pretium, procedere recte* | *Qui mæchis non vultis*—[to the right] Hor. Sat. 2. 1. I. | *—Metuat doti deprenſa.*—[to the right] Ibid. || *LONDON:* | Printed for *Jacob Tonfon,* within *Gray's-Inn-Gate* next | *Gray's-Inn-Lane.* 1700.

*Half-title: A1*: || THE | Way of the World, | A | COMEDY. ||

*Collation:* 4°. *A*⁴ a² B–M⁴ N², 52 leaves, pp. [12] 1–89 *90–92,* \$2 (-a², N²) signed.

HT] ‖ ‖ THE | Way of the World. | A | COMEDY. ‖

*Contents: A1:* half-title (verso blank). *A2:* title (verso blank). A3: ‖ ‖ 'To the Right Honourable | RALPH | Earl of *MOUNTAGUE,* &c.' (text [cap²]). Signed on a1ᵛ: 'Will. Congreve.' ‖ a2: 'PROLOGUE, | Spoken by Mr. *Betterton.*' | [40 ll. *'O²F thoſe few Fools, who with ill Stars are curs'd,'*]. a2ᵛ: 'Perſonæ Dramatis.' (with cast) B1: HT with text (cap⁴) headed 'ACT I. SCENE I.' ‖ N1ᵛ: ‖ ‖ 'EPILOGUE. | Spoken by Mrs. *Bracegirdle.*' | [36 ll. *'A²Fter our* Epilogue *this Crowd diſmiſſes,'*]. N2ᵛ: ‖ ‖ 'BOOKS Printed for *Jacob Tonſon* | within *Gray's-Inn-Gate* next *Gray's- | Inn-Lane.*'

RT] *The Way of the World.* [*VVorld.* H2; *The VVay of the VVorld.* H2ᵛ, N1. RT frequently partially cropped]

CW] *A3* What- [Whatever] a2ᵛ THE B4ᵛ *Wit.* C1 *Wit:* [*Wit.*] D4ᵛ Uncle, E3 un- [unleſs] F1 (Chim-) ney. [ney—] G1ᵛ Ani- [Animoſity] H3ᵛ Natu- [Natural,] I4ᵛ *Enter* K4ᵛ Mrs. *Fain.* L4ᵛ *Enter* [*Lady.*] M2 ſubſi [ſubſiſtance] M4 Sir. *Wil.* [Sir *Wil.*]

*Type:* text (B2): 38 ll., 175(187) x 108 mm., 92R.

*Notes:* N2, which is torn, has been bound so that the verso of the leaf faces N1ᵛ. Page numbers in headline against outer margin of type-page except for '1,' centered in parentheses. Bound in red cloth. W. & M. 249. Wing C5878.

PR3364 .W3 1700

# 78. 1706

[*title*] as in 1700 (77.) except for | As it is Acted at the | THEATRE in *Lincolns-Inn-Fields,* | . . . | HIS    MAJESTY's . . . ‖ [5    lines] ‖ The SECOND EDITION, Reviſed. ‖ *LONDON:* | Printed for *Jacob Tonſon;* and Sold by *James Knapton* at the | *Crown* in St. *Paul's* Church-yard, *George Strahan* over againſt | the Royal Exchange in *Cornhill,* and *Egbert Sanger* at the | Poſt-Houſe near the *Temple*-Gate in *Fleetſtreet.* 1706.

*Collation:* 4°. A–I⁴ K², 38 leaves, pp. [8] 1–68 [misprinting 54 as 55 and 55 as 54], $2 (-K2) signed.

HT] ‖ ‖ THE | Way of the World. ‖

*Contents:* A1: title (verso blank). A2: dedicatory epistle (cap³). A3ᵛ: prologue (cap²). A4: epilogue (cap²). A4ᵛ: dramatis personae (with cast). B1: HT with text (cap³).

RT] as in 1700 (77.) but with no variants.

CW] A4ᵛ THE B3 (Obſtina-)cy C3 Mrs. *Fan.* [Mrs. *Fain.*] D4ᵛ *Wait.* E4ᵛ me F4ᵛ Nay G3ᵛ (Hare's-) gall H4ᵛ (Mar-)riages, I4ᵛ of [CW cropped on I1, I3]

*Type:* text (C4): 42 ll., 194(206) x 123 mm., 92R.

*Notes:* Page numbers in headline against outer margin of type-page except for '1,' centered in brackets. In the dramatis personæ Fainall is described as in love with 'Mrs. *Marword.*' This copy may be an uncorrected state of the Harvard copy: in two places it retains the 1700 readings (A2ᵛ, 1. 27, 'laugh out'; I2, ll. 31–2, 'ſtand by a Trial.') rather than the later readings of the Harvard copy ('laugh at' and 'ſtand a Trial.') as recorded by Davis. Bound in mottled brown boards with green leather over spine. Purchased from Stonehill in 1950.

PR3364 .W3 1706

## 79.  1710

*Notes:* A separate binding of the text of the play from the 1710 Hills edition of the plays (100.). The title page has no imprint date. Bound in mottled boards.

PR3364 .W3 1710

## 80.  1733

[*title*] identical with *Way of the World* section title in 1733 *Dramatick Works* (102.).

*Notes:* A separate binding of the text of the single play from the *Dramatick Works* (102.). Bound in blue cloth.

PR3364 .W3 1733

## 81.  1735

[*title*] identical with *Way of the World* section title of 1735 edition of the *Plays.*

*Notes:* A separate binding of the text of the single play from 1735 *Plays* (103.) with the blank leaves ³*E12* and χ1 excluded. Bound in orange cloth.

PR3364 .W3 1735

## 82. 1755

THE | WAY of the WORLD: | A | COMEDY. | Written by Mr. CONGREVE. | [3-line motto from Horace and ack.] | *EDINBURGH:* | Printed for G. HAMILTON and J. BALFOUR. | [partial rule] | M, DCC, LV.

*Collation:* 12°. *A⁴* B–N⁴ O1, 53 leaves, pp. *1–3* 4–7 *8 9 10–11* 12–104 *105* 106, $1 signed.

HT] THE | WAY OF THE WORLD.

*Contents: A1:* title (verso blank). *A2:* dedicatory epistle (cap²). *A4ᵛ:* prologue (cap²). B1ᵛ: dramatis personae (with cast). B2: HT with text (cap³). O1: epilogue (cap²).

RT] THE WAY OF THE WORLD.

CW] *A4ᵛ Some* C1ᵛ *Mira.* [*Mira*] E4ᵛ *Milla.* G4ᵛ the I4ᵛ confident, L4ᵛ reſolv'd M4ᵛ Sir

*Type:* text (C2): 39 ll., 131(139) x 70 mm., 66R.

*Notes:* The edition follows the scene divisions of the 1710 *Works.* The second portion of Scene III, Act II, is misnumbered Scene IV, but Scene IV is properly numbered. No press figures. Bound in blue cloth.

PR3364 .W3 1755

## 83. 1756

[in black and red] THE | Way of the World. | A | COMEDY. || Written by Mr. CONGREVE. || [3-line motto from Horace and ack.] || [triangle of fleurons] || London: | Printed for J. and R. TONSON, in the Strand. | M DCC LVI.

*Collation:* 12°. A¹² (A1 missing) B–D¹², 47 leaves, pp. [10] *1* 2–82 *83–84,* $5 signed.

HT] [rect. of fleuron type orn. (19 x 72)] | THE | Way of the World. ||

*Contents:* A1ʳ⁻ᵛ: lacking (blank?). A2: title (verso blank); A3: dedicatory epistle (fact⁴) headed by double row of fleurons. A5ᵛ: prologue headed by triple row of fleurons. On A6: triangle of fleurons. A6ᵛ: dramatis personae (with cast). A7: HT with text (fact[6]). D12: epilogue headed by double row of fleurons. On D12$^v$: triangle of fleurons.

RT] *The* WAY *of the* WORLD.

CW] A12$^v$ and B12$^v$ Mrs. C12$^v$ My

*Type:* text (A8): 42 ll., 139(146) x 73 mm., 66R.

*Notes:* The factotums are made up of type ornaments. The acts are separated by a double or triple row of type ornaments. The second page of the prologue (A6) is headed 'EPILOGUE.' Bound in orange cloth.

PR3364 .W3 1756

## 84. 1759

[*title*] identical with *Way of the World* section-title of 1736 Dublin edition of the *Works* (113.)

*Notes:* A separate binding of the text of the single play from *Works* (Dublin, 1736), with the prefixed leaves omitted. See 113. Bound in red cloth.

PR3364 .W3 1759

## 85. 1774

THE | WAY   of   the   WORLD. | A | COMEDY. | Written   by | *Mr.* CONGREVE. ‖ [3-line   motto   from   Horace   and   ack.] ‖ [triangle   of fleurons] ‖ LONDON: | Printed for W. FOX, in *Holborn.* | [partial rule] | M DCC LXXIV.

*Collation:* 12°. A$^8$ B–D$^{12}$ E$^3$, 47 leaves, pp. *1–11* 12–92 *93–94*, plate (opp. sig. A1), $5 (-A5, E3) signed.

HT] ‖‖ THE | *WAY* of the *WORLD.* ‖

*Contents:* A1: title (verso blank). A2: dedicatory epistle (cap$^2$) headed by double row of fleurons. A4: Steele's commendatory poem (cap$^2$) headed by orn. [scrollwork (4 x 71)]. A5: prologue (cap$^2$). A5$^v$: dramatis personae (with cast). A6: HT with text (cap$^2$). E3: epilogue (cap$^2$) headed by row of type orn. [ornamented x's].

RT] *The* WAY *of the* WORLD.

CW] A8ᵛ *Fain.* B10 *Milla-[Milla.]* C8ᵛ Mrs. [Mrs] D12ᵛ *Fain.*

*Type:* text (B4): 42 ll., 138(146) x 74 mm., 65R.

*Notes:* No press figures. Acts II, IV, and V are headed by a rule. The title page is preceded by an unsigned disjunct engraving which has no relevance to the play and is clearly misplaced: one man with his hand on his sword is restrained by another; a third lies on the ground, apparently wounded, while a woman looks on in distress. The engraved surface measures 122 x 73 mm. Bound in blue cloth.

PR3364 .W3]1774

## 86. 1774

Another copy.

*Notes:* This copy is bound with the other Congreve plays as the fifth in a volume containing Rowe's *Jane Shore* and *The Fair Penitent.* The same engraving precedes the title page.

PR3362 .F6 1774

## 87. 1780

*BELL'S EDITION.* | [rod (27 mm.)] | THE | *WAY OF THE WORLD.* | A COMEDY, | *As written by WILLIAM CONGREVE.* | DISTINGUISHING ALSO THE | VARIATIONS OF THE THEATRE, | AS PERFORMED AT THE | 𝔗𝔥𝔢𝔞𝔱𝔯𝔢=𝔯𝔬𝔶𝔞𝔩 𝔦𝔫 𝔇𝔯𝔲𝔯𝔶=𝔏𝔞𝔫𝔢. | Regulated from the Prompt-Book, | *By PERMISSION of the MANAGERS,* | By Mr. HOPKINS, Prompter. | [3-line motto from Horace and ack.] | [John Bell's monogram] | *LONDON:* | Printed for JOHN BELL, at the Britiſh Library in the *Strand.* | [partial rule] | M DCC LXXX.

*Collation:* 12°. π² A–F⁶ G², 40 leaves, pp. *1–5* 6–79 *80* [misprinting 63 as 39], $3 (-G2) signed.

HT] THE | WAY OF THE WORLD.

*Contents:* π1: title (verso blank). π2: prologue. π2ᵛ: dramatis personae. A1: HT with text (cap⁴). G2ᵛ: epilogue.

RT] THE WAY OF THE WORLD.

CW] A6ᵛ *Pet.* B2 *Mrs Fain.* [*Mrs. Fain.*] C6ᵛ *Mrs Mar.* D6ᵛ Milla. E6ᵛ *Wait.* F6ᵛ what

*Type:* text (B4): 42 ll., 141(150) x 75 mm., 67R.

*Notes:* Press figures are present as follows: A6ᵛ-2, B6ᵛ-2, C6ᵛ-1, D6ᵛ-1, E6ᵛ-1, F6ᵛ-2. In the headline next fold (except A4 where the act and page numbers have been reversed) 'Act I.' and according to act. The last line of the prologue has been cropped. The play follows the scene divisions of the 1710 *Works.* Despite the title page claim, there is no indication of acting deletions or additions. Bound in orange cloth.

PR3364 .W3 1780

## 88. 1796

THE | *WAY OF THE WORLD.* | [partial double rule] | A | COMEDY. | [partial double rule] | By WILLIAM CONGREVE, ESQ. | [partial double rule] | ADAPTED FOR | *THEATRICAL REPRESENTATION,* | AS PERFORMED AT THE | THEATRE-ROYAL, COVENT-GARDEN. | [partial double rule] | REGULATED FROM THE PROMPT-BOOK, | *By Permission of the Manager.* ||| The Lines distinguished by inverted Commas, are omitted in the Representation. ||| LONDON: | [partial double rule] | *Printed for, and under the Direction of,* | GEORGE CAWTHORN, 𝔅𝔯𝔦𝔱𝔦𝔰𝔥 𝔏𝔦𝔟𝔯𝔞𝔯𝔶, STRAND. | [partial rule] | M DCC XCVI.

*Collation:* 12°. A⁴ B–L⁶, 64 leaves, pp. *i–iii* iv–viii *ix* x *xi–xii 13* 14–128 [59 misnumbered as 55], plate (opp. sig. A1) $3 (-A3, C1) signed.

HT] [orn.: as on HT, 21.] | THE | WAY OF THE WORLD. |||

*Contents:* A1: title (verso blank). A2: life of Congreve (title within double rules). B1: prologue (title within double rules). B2: blank. B2ᵛ: dramatis personae (with cast) [title within double rules]. B3: HT with text. On L6: epilogue (title within double rules).

RT] THE WAY OF THE WORLD.

*Type:* text (F1): 30 ll., 112(120) x 68 mm., 76R.

*Notes:* Press figures are present as follows: C4ᵛ-1, F6ᵛ-1, G1ᵛ-1, K4ᵛ-2, K6ᵛ-3. No CW. In the headline against fold '*Act I.*' and according to act in italic. Acts are separated by double rules. The title page is preceded by a disjunct engraving of Miss De Camp as Foible. The engraved surface measures 113 x 77 mm. and is signed on the left *'Roberts Pinxit'* and on the right *'P. Thomson Sculpsit'*; the imprint date is July 8, 1796. The CG cast listed is that of the January 13, 1790 performance except for Mrs. Platt as Mincing (Avery, p. 216). The play is bound as the first play in a volume containing additionally *Samson Agonistes* (1796), John Hoole's *Timanthes* (1795), and General John Burgoyne's *Richard Coeur de Lion* (1806). Each is signed and paged individually; the volume has the following title page: *'BELL'S* | BRITISH THEATRE. | [partial double rule] | CONSISTING OF | *THE MOST ESTEEMED* | 𝕰𝖓𝖌𝖑𝖎𝖘𝖍 𝕻𝖑𝖆𝖞𝖘. ||| VOL. VIII. ||| *LONDON*: | PRINTED FOR, AND UNDER THE DIRECTION OF, | GEORGE CAWTHORN, BRITISH LIBRARY, STRAND. | [orn.] | 1797.'

PR3364 .W3 1796

# *A Pindarique Ode, Humbly Offered to the Queen.* 1706

## 89. 1706

[within double rules] A | PINDARIQUE | ODE, | Humbly Offer'd to the | QUEEN, | ON THE | Victorious Progreſs of Her MAJESTY's Arms, un- | der the Conduct of the Duke of MARLBOROUGH. || To which is prefix'd | A DISCOURSE on the PINDARIQUE ODE. || By Mr. *CONGREVE.* || *—Operoſa parvus* | *Carmina fingo.* Hor. Ode 2. L. 4. | *Tuque dum procedis, Io triumphe* | *Non ſemel dicemus, Io triumphe* | *Civitas omnis; dabimusq; Divis* | *Thura benignis.* Ibid. || *LONDON:* | Printed for *Jacob Tonſon*, within *Grays-Inn* Gate next | *Grays-Inn* Lane. 1706.

*Collation:* 2°. π1 A–C² D1, 8 leaves, pp. [*6*] 1–10, \$1 signed.

HT] ‖ ‖ ODE.

*Contents:* π1: title (verso blank) A1: ‖ ‖ 'A | DISCOURSE | ON THE | PINDARIQUE ODE.' B1: HT with text (cap²). On D1ᵛ: *'FINIS.'*

RT] A1ᵛ-A2: A Diſcourſe on the | Pindarique ODE. A2ᵛ: A Diſcourſe on the Pindarique ODE.

CW] A2ᵛ ODE. B2ᵛ Thy C2ᵛ Tho'

*Type:* text (B2ᵛ): 25 ll., 231(267 [notes below the direction-line frequently extend the page to 270]) x 154 mm., 198R.

*Notes:* Page numbers are centered in brackets. In pamphlet binder. Pforzheimer 210.

PR3364 .P52 1706

## Ovid's *Art of Love*, Book III. 1709

### 90. 1709

[in black and red] OVID's | ART of LOVE. | IN THREE BOOKS. |
Together with his | REMEDY of LOVE. | Tranſlated into Engliſh
Verſe | BY | Several Eminent Hands. || To which are added, | THE
COURT of LOVE, | A Tale from CHAUCER. | AND THE | HISTORY
of LOVE. || ADORN'D with CUTS. || London: Printed for Jacob
Tonſon at Grays-Inn-Gate, next | Grays-Inn-Lane. 1709.

*Half-titles:* B1: || OVID's | Art of Love. | Book the Firſt. || Z6: || THE
| COURT of LOVE. | A | TALE, | FROM | CHAUCER. || 2A8: THE |
HISTORY | OF | LOVE. | A | POEM: | IN | A LETTER to a LADY. ||
By Mr. CHARLES HOPKINS. || Eſt quoque Carminibus meritas
celebrare Puellas | Dos mea, -----Ovid. | -----Utinam modo dicere poſſem, |
Carmina digna dea, certè eſt dea carmina digna. Ibid. || Printed for
J. Tonſon. 1709.

*Collation:* 8°. π1A⁴(-A4) B⁸(±B2) C–Q⁸ (±Q5, –Q6) R-2H⁸ χ1, 244
leaves, pp. [10] 1–174 179–235 238–348 *349–350* 351–368 *369–374* 375–482
[=476] [2], plates [7] (opp. sigs. A1, B2, H6, N1, S5ᵛ, Z7, 2A8.)

*Contents:* π1ʳ⁻ᵛ: blank. A1: title (verso blank). A2: [orn.: coat of arms sur-
mounted with crown, rampant lions at sides; at bottom 'VIVIT POST FUNERA
VIRTUS' (35 x 94)] | 'To the Right Honourable | RICHARD, | Earl of
Burlington.' [42 ll. 'O²UR Poet's Rules, in eaſie numbers tell']. On A3ᵛ: orn.
[feminine head with border of serpent with its tail in its mouth, surrounded by
foliage.] Signed on the left 'O: Elliger invent:' and on the right 'H. Elant fecit:'
(68 x 111). B1: *Art of Love* half-title (verso blank). B2: text of *Art of Love* and
notes. N1: text of third book of *Art of Love.* Q5ᵛ: notes on third book. S5ᵛ: text
of *Remedy of Love* and notes; Z2 text of Ovid's *Art of Beauty*; Z6: *Court of Love*
half-title (verso blank). Z7: *The Court of Love* text; 2A8: *History of Love* half-title
(verso blank). 2B1 || || 'To Her GRACE the | DUTCHESS | OF | GRAFTON.'
(cap³). Signed on 2B2ᵛ: 'Charles Hopkins.' 2B3: *History of Love* text. χ1ʳ⁻ᵛ:
blank.

RT] OVID's || | Art of Love. || B2ᵛ-E5, H6ᵛ-L6, N1ᵛ-Q5; Notes on the
Firſt Book. E6ᵛ-H5ᵛ [Book (no period) F3]; Notes on the Second Book. L7-
M8ᵛ; Notes on the Third Book. Q7-S5; Ovid's || | Remedy of Love. || S6ᵛ-Y1
[Love (no period) T4]; Notes on the | Remedy of Love. Y2ᵛ-Z1; OVID's || |
Art of Beauty. || Z2ᵛ-Z5; The Court of Love. || Z7ᵛ-2A7ᵛ; The Hiſtory of Love.
2B3ᵛ-2H8ᵛ [Love, 2G2ᵛ].

CW] B8ᵛ Doubt D8ᵛ On F8ᵛ (men-)tion H8ᵛ Now K8ᵛ A M8ᵛ OVID's [OVID's] P1ᵛ Now, [Now] Q4ᵛ Thus, S3ᵛ green T8ᵛ (For X8ᵛ A Z2ᵛ But 2A1ᵛ From 2C8ᵛ A 2E8ᵛ Ah! 2G8ᵛ In [no CW on H3ᵛ, L6, 2E2ᵛ, 2F3ᵛ, 2F4ᵛ, 2F8, 2H5]

*Signing and numbering:* $4(-A3) signed. Following errors in signature and pagination: 2A3 misnumbered as 2A4; p. 355 as 855. The following symbols may function as press figures: I8ᵛ-*, K2ᵛ-⊣, N8-⊣, 07-*, 08-*, P2ᵛ-*, P7ᵛ-*, 2B1ᵛ-*, 2C7-*.

*Type:* text (N4ᵛ): 18 ll., 139(160) x 94 mm., 79 mm. for 10 ll.

*Notes:* In addition to the cancel leaves noted in the collation, stubs are present between A4-B1, B7-8, H3-4, L8-M1, S3-4, Z2-3, 2A1-2, presumably the binding stubs of the engravings. The 7 disjunct engravings range in size from 155 x 98 to 176 x 112; three are unsigned, three by L. du Guernier, and one by M. Vander Gucht. The engraving preceding Congreve's translation (facing N1) depicts Venus reclining with Cupids around her. The engraved surface measures 165 x 107 and is signed on the left 'F. Albane pinxit' and on the right 'L. du Guernier Sculp.' The three books of the *Art of Love* have head-titles which attribute the first and third to Dryden and Congreve respectively; the typography of the head-title of Book I differs from the other two. Each book is followed by notes. The two books of the *Remedy*, the *Art of Beauty*, the *Court of Love*, and the *History of Love* also have head-titles. Bound in brown leather. Macdonald 40. Case 252.

PA6522 .A3 1709

## *Semele.* 1710

### 91. 1744

THE | STORY | OF | SEMELE. | As it is Perform'd at the | THEATRE-ROYAL *in* Covent-Garden. ‖ Alter'd from the SEMELE of Mr. WILLIAM CONGREVE: ‖ Set to Muſick by Mr. GEORGE FREDERICK HANDEL. ‖ [orn. T25] ‖ ‖ *LONDON:* | Printed for J. and R. TONSON in the *Strand*. | [partial rule] | M DCC XLIV. | [Price One Shilling.]

*Collation:* 4°. A–C⁴ D², 14 leaves, pp. *1–5* 6–28. $2 (-D2) signed.

HT] [orn. (T11)] | The STORY of | SEMELE. ‖

*Contents:* A1: title (verso blank) A2: 'ARGUMENT.' [below: orn. (T12)] A2ᵛ: 'DRAMATIS PERSONÆ.' A3: HT with text (orn. initial⁴) headed 'PART I. SCENE I.' On D2ᵛ: 'FINIS.' | orn. (T13).

RT] *The* STORY *of* | *SEMELE.* [on D2ᵛ *The* STORY, &c.]

CW] A3 Cadm. [*Cadm.*] B4ᵛ *Chorus* C4ᵛ SONG.

*Type:* text (A4): 33 ll., 197(212) x 125 mm. 119R.

*Notes: Semele* was first published in the 1710 *Works.* Presumably this first separate publication is the text of the opera as it was performed on February 10, 1744. (*London Stage,* Part 3, p. 1088). Parts II and III are headed by small ornaments. Bound in green cloth. Purchased in 1956.

PR3364 .S4 1744

## *The Story of Orpheus and Eurydice* and *The Fable of Cyparissus,* Ovid's *Metamorphoses,* Book X. 1717

## 92. 1727

[*vol. titles*] *vol. 1:* OVID's | *METAMORPHOSES,* | In FIFTEEN BOOKS. | Tranſlated by | [5 lines braced to right and left] *Mr.* Dryden. *Mr.* Rowe. | *Mr.* Addiſon. *Mr.* Pope. | *Dr.* Garth. *Mr.* Gay. | *Mr.* Mainwaring. *Mr.* Euſden. | *Mr.* Congreve. *Mr.* Croxall. | *And other* EMINENT HANDS. || *Publiſh'd by Sir* SAMUEL GARTH, *M.D.* || Adorn'd with SCULPTURES. || VOLUME *the* FIRST. || The THIRD EDITION. || *LONDON:* | Printed for J. TONSON in the *Strand.* | [partial rule] | M DCC XXVII. *vol. 2:* OVID's | *METAMORPHOSES,* | IN | FIFTEEN BOOKS. | *Tranſlated by the moſt Eminent Hands.* | [as on vol. 1. except for vol. no. and omission of statement of publication by Garth]

*Collation:* 12°. *vol. 1:* π1 A–N¹²χ1, 158 leaves, pp. [18] *i* ii–lii [4] *1–3* 4–40 *41–43* 44–81 *82–85* 86–115 *116–119* 120–159 *160–163* 164–198 *199–201* 202–239 *240* [2]; *vol. 2:* π1 A⁶ B–Q¹²χ1, 188 leaves, pp. [14] *1* 2–39 *40–43* 44–87 *88–91* 92–124 *125–127* 128–165 *166–169* 170–205 *206–209* 210–236 *237–239* 240–284 *285–287* 288–306 *307–308* 309–315 *316–319* 320–359 *360* [2].

*Contents: vol. 1:* π1ʳ⁻ᵛ blank; A1 blank; A1ᵛ engraving; A2 vol. title (verso blank); A3 blank; A3 engraving; A4 [orn.: T3] | 'TO HER | ROYAL HIGHNESS.' (orn. initial³). Signed on A8 'S. GARTH.' A8ᵛ blank; A9 [orn.: T2] | 'PREFACE.' (fact⁵) C11 [orn.: T50] | 'CONTENTS.' || D1 blank; D1 engraving; D2 [orn.: T43] | 'OVID's | *METAMORPHOSES.* | BOOK I. | *Tranſlated by Mr.* JOHN DRYDEN.' (orn. initial⁶) D2-N12: text of the first six books. N12ᵛ blank; χ1ʳ⁻ᵛ blank. *vol. 2:* π1ʳ⁻ᵛ blank; A1 blank; A1ᵛ engraving;

A2 vol. title (verso blank); A3 [orn.: T50] | 'CONTENTS.' ‖ ; on A5$^v$ orn. [T29]; A6 blank; A6$^v$ engraving; B1-Q12 text of books 7–15; Q12$^v$ blank; χ1$^{r-v}$ blank.

RT] *PREFACE*. vol. 1, A9$^v$-C10$^v$ [*PREFACE* (no period) A12] OVID'*s Metamorphoſes*. vol. 1, D2$^v$-N12 [*Metamorpohſes*. I6]; vol. 2, B1$^v$-Q12.

CW] *vol. 1:* A12$^v$ --- *Madidis* B11$^v$ *Illum* [—*Illum*] C12$^v$ OVID'*s* [D1 blank] F2$^v$ *Corynth* [*Corinth*] G5 OVID'*s* [G5$^v$ blank] G12$^v$ "And ["(And] K8 OVID'*s* [K8$^v$ blank] M12$^v$ *The vol. 2:* A5$^v$ OVID'*s* [A6 blank] B1$^v$ Yet' [Yet,] I12$^v$ But M8 The [Then] N2$^v$ Wit [With] N8 That [For] O9$^v$ Long [O10: engraving] P12$^v$ The [Approximately ⅓ of the pages have no CW.]

*Signing and numbering:* $5 signed (-*vol. 1* D3, F3, I4, K4, L3; *vol. 2* A4.5, B3, C4, D4, N4, Q5; + *vol. 1* L6). On $1 of each signed gathering (except *vol. 2* sig. C1) in signature-line next fold 'VOL. I.' (except comma after number on *vol. 1* sig. N1) and according to vol. with rom. numbers. Press figures are present as follows: *vol. 1:* A12-4, B11$^v$-5, C12-4, D5$^v$-5, E12-4, F12-5, F12$^v$-7, G11$^v$-4, H3$^v$-7, I5$^v$-7, L8-4, M8-8; *vol. 2:* B2$^v$-7, C12$^v$-7, D11$^v$-7, E11$^v$-5, F7-5, G12-4, H8-8, I12-5, K6$^v$-5, L7$^v$-4, M12$^v$-5, N1$^v$-4, O1$^v$-4, P5$^v$-8. Following errors in pagination: *vol. 1:* xlvii misnumbered as xlviii, 114 as 113. *vol. 2:* 130 misnumbered as 136, 158 as 185, 231 as 131, 347 as 345.

*Type:* text (vol. 1, E4): 30 ll., 127(136) x 74 mm., 85 R.

*Notes:* In the headline next fold 'Book I.' and according to book in rom. numbers. Each book is headed by a headpiece ornament, a HT, and a statement of the translator in one or two lines (except for Book IV.). Thirteen of the fifteen books follow the statement of the translator with a 1 or 2-line title for the story of the book or the first story in the book. Six of the thirteen follow this title with the translator's name in one line. Book IV. omits the statement of translator but provides a title for the first story and the translator's name of that story. The text of each book begins with a 5 or 6-line factotum or orn. initial. The engraving preceding the title of each volume depicts persons in Roman attire before a bust of Ovid on a pedestal inscribed 'OVID's | *Metamorphoſes* | TranSlated | *by the* | *MJt. Eminent* | Hands'. The engraved surface, which is unsigned, measures 118 x 76 mm. The engraving preceding the dedicatory epistle (*vol. 1*, A4) is from the Kneller portrait of the Princess of Wales, Princess Caroline. Signed on the left '*G. Kneller* [two abbreviations illegible] *Pinx:*' and on the right '*M. Vdr. Gucht Sculp:*', the engraved surface measures 131 x 75 mm. Each of the fifteen books is preceded by a conjugate unsigned engraving depicting a scene from the book and dedicated to a feminine member of the nobility or distinguished person. An additional engraving appears in Book XIV (*vol. 2*, O10). Bound in brown leather, the edition has the bookplate of Philip Earl Stanhope. Macdonald includes the first edition as Macdonald 41. Case 298 (1) (c), 298 (2) (c).

PA6522 .M2 1717

## *To His Grace the Duke of Newcastle* (Dedication to Dryden's *Dramatic Works*). 1717

### 93. 1717

[*General title in vol. 1 only*] The DRAMATICK | WORKS | OF | *John Dryden*, E∫q; | IN | SIX VOLUMES. ‖ ‖ *LONDON:* | Printed for *J. Ton∫on:* And Sold by *R. Knaplock,* | *W. Taylor, W. Mears, J. Browne, W. Churchill,* | *E. Symon,* and *J. Brotherton.* M DCC XVII.

[*vol. titles*] *vol. 1:* The DRAMATICK | WORKS | OF | *John Dryden,* E∫q; | VOLUME *the* FIRST. | CONTAINING,

| | |
|---|---|
| An ESSAY *of* DRA-<br>MATICK POESIE.<br>*The* WILD GALLANT.<br>*The* RIVAL LADIES. | *The* INDIAN QUEEN.<br>*The* INDIAN EMPE-<br>ROR: *Or, the Con-*<br>*que∫t of* MEXICO. |

‖ ‖ Printed in the YEAR M DCC XVII.

*vol 2:* [as in vol. 1 except for vol. no., list of plays in seven lines, separation of titles by double vertical rules instead of braces but with imprint] *LONDON:* | Printed for JACOB TONSON at *Shake∫pear's Head* | over-again∫t *Katherine-Street* in the *Strand.* | M DCC XVII.

*vol. 3–6:* [as in vol. 2 except for vol. no., list of plays in five to seven lines, and separation of titles by single vertical rule in vol. 6]

*Collation:* 12°. *vol. 1:* $A^3$ ($\pm A^2$) $a^{12}$ $A^4$-$A^{12}$ B-$M^{12}$ $N^{12}$(-N7 + $NO^{12}$) O-$P^{12}$ $Q^6$, pp. *1–6* [24] *7–15* 16–83 *84–93* 94–164 *165–183* 184–248 *249–253* 254–293 *294–302* [22] *303–305* 306–370 *371–372; vol. 2:* A-$S^{12}T^6$, pp. *1–15* 16–81 *82–89* 90–160 *161–171* 172–253 *254–281* 282–367 *368–381* 382–443 *444; vol. 3:* A-$G^{12}H^4$ $1HI^6$ $2HI^2$ $H^5$-$H^{12}$ I-$S^{12}$, pp. *1–31* 32–94 *95–99* 100–175 *176* [16] *177–187* 188–268 *269–283* 284–356 *357–369* 370–430 *431–432; vol. 4:* A-$T^{12}$, pp. *1–29* 30–70 *71–89* 90–167 *168–195* 196–271 *272–283* 284–365 *366–375* 376–454 *455–456; vol. 5:* A-$R^{12}$, pp. *1–14* 15–37 *38–41* 42–120 *121–135* 136–219 *220–233* 234–306 *307–313* 314–362 *363–365* 366–374 *375–377* 378 *379* 380–407 *408; vol. 6:* A-$X^{12}Y^4$, pp. *1–14* 15–21 *22–27* 28–141 *142–153* 154–230 *231–247* 248–279 *280–283* 284–349 *350–363* 364–407 *408–421* 422–497 *498–503* 504–507 *508–512.*

*Contents: vol. 1:* A1 blank; A1ᵛ Dryden portrait; A2 general title (verso blank); A3 vol. title (verso blank); a1 [orn.: coat of arms with a horse on the left and falcon on the right, below 'VICIT AMOR PATRIA' (31 x 73)] | 'To His GRACE the | Duke of *Newca∫tle,* | *Lord Chamberlain of His Ma-* | *je∫ty's Hou∫hold,* &c.'

(orn. initial[3]); signed on a12 'William Congreve.' a12$^v$ blank; A4 *Essay of Dramatic Poesie* half-title (verso blank); A5 dedicatory epistle headed by orn. (T30); A7$^v$ address to the reader; A8 *Essay* text headed by orn. [T33] and HT; on D6 orn. [sun shining on earth in octagonal frame, ornamented with cornucopias and foliage (57 x 63)]; D6$^v$ blank; D7 *Wild Gallant* half-title (verso blank); D8 preface headed by orn. (T69); on D8$^v$ orn. [dog baying at moon (26 x 46)]; D9 original prologue; D10 prologue at revival; D10$^v$ dramatis personae; D11 *WG* text headed by orn. (T34) and HT; on G10$^v$ orn. [T15]; G11 original epilogue; G11$^v$ epilogue at revival; on G12 orn. [Plomer 102]; G12$^v$ blank; H1 *Rival Ladies* half-title (verso blank); H2 dedicatory epistle headed by orn. [T36]; H7 prologue; H7$^v$ dramatis personae; H8 *RL* text headed by orn. [T37]; on L4$^v$ orn. [skull on pedestal with foliage (54 x 60)]; L5 *Indian Queen* half-title (verso blank); L6 prologue; L6$^v$ dramatis personae; L7 *IQ* text headed by orn. [T28] and HT; N3$^v$ epilogue; N4 *Indian Emperor* half-title (verso blank); N5 dedicatory epistle headed by orn. [T34]; NO1$^v$ blank; NO2 *Defence of an Essay of Dramatic Poesie* text headed by orn. [T86] and HT; on NO12 orn. [T32]; NO12$^v$ statement of connection of *IE* to *IQ;* N8 prologue; N8$^v$ dramatis personae; N9 *IE* text headed by orn. [T33] and HT; Q6 epilogue; Q6$^v$ blank.

*vol. 2:* A1$^v$ Dryden portrait; A2 vol. title (verso blank); A3 *Secret Love;* D7 *Sir Martin Mar-all;* G10 *The Tempest;* L8 *An Evening's Love;* Q5 *Tyrannick Love.*

*vol. 3:* A1$^v$ Dryden portrait; A2 vol. title (verso blank); A3 *Conquest of Granada, Part I*; E1 *Conquest of Granada, Part II*; 1 HI 1 *Defence of the Epilogue;* H5 *Marriage a la Mode;* M4 *The Assignation;* P12 *Amboyna.*

*vol. 4:* A1$^v$ Dryden portrait; A2 vol. title (verso blank); A3 *State of Innocence;* C12 *Aureng-Zebe;* H2 *All for Love;* M5 *Limberham;* Q4 *Oedipus.*

*vol. 5:* A1$^v$ Dryden portrait; A2 vol. title (verso blank); A3 *Troilus and Cressida;* F2 *The Spanish Friar;* K4 *The Duke of Guise;* N12 *Vindication of the Duke of Guise;* Q2 *Albion and Albanius.*

*vol. 6:* A1$^v$ Dryden portrait; A2 vol. title (verso blank); A3 *Don Sebastian;* F12 *Amphitryon;* K9 *Cleomenes;* P8 *King Arthur;* S2 *Love Triumphant;* X11 *Dialogue and Secular Masque;* Y4$^v$ Tonson book advertisement.

RT] *vol. 1: DEDICATION.* a1$^v$-a12; *The Epiſtle Dedicatory.* A5$^v$-A7; *An Essay of Dramatick Poeſie.* A8$^v$-D6; *The* WILD GALLANT. D11$^v$-G10$^v$; *The Epiſtle Dedicatory.* H2$^v$-H6$^v$. *The* RIVAL LADIES. H8$^v$-L4$^v$; *The* INDIAN QUEEN. L7$^v$-N3; *The Epistle Dedicatory.* N5$^v$-NO1; *Defence of an Eſſay | of Dramatick Poeſie.* NO2$^v$-NO12; *The* INDIAN EMPEROR. N9$^v$-Q5$^v$ [EMPEROR (no period) O4, Q2; EMPEKOR. O9; EWPEROR. (M inverted) O11]

*Note:* Each play in vols. 2-6 has separate running-title as above.

CW] *vol. 1:* a11$^v$ ſingu-[ſingularly] G9$^v$ *Iſa,* [*Iſa.*] I6 *Hippolito,* [*Hippolito*] N6$^v$ irregu-[irregular] NO1 A [NO1$^v$ blank] NO12$^v$ PRO-[PROLOGUE.] P12$^v$ *Chr. Pr.* [no cw on G10$^v$, H10]

*Signing and numbering:* $5 signed (-*vol. 1,* Q4.5; *vol. 2,* T4.5; *vol. 3,* 1 HI 4.5,

2 HI 2, M3; *vol. 6*, Y3.4; + *vol. 1*, L6; *vol. 4*, M6). On $1 of each signed gathering in signature-line next fold 'VOL. I.' and according to volume (except vol. 1, sig. a, and vol. 6, sig. L1, which has 'VOL. IV.') with rom. numbers. No press figures. Following errors in pagination and signatures: *vol. 1*: 282 misnumbered as 283, 283 as 282, 286 as 287, 287 as 286; *vol. 3*: 347 as 247; *vol. 4*: sig. Q5 missigned as O5; 298 misnumbered as 266, 310 as 301; *vol. 5*: 119 misnumbered as 11, 205 as 20, 251 as 25, all with terminal digit dropped; *vol. 6*: 276 misnumbered as 279, 323 unnumbered, 427 misnumbered as 327, 504 as 500.

*Type:* text (*vol. 1*, E2): 38 ll., 123(130) x 73 mm., 64 R.

*Notes*: All plays, the *Essay of Dramatic Poesie*, the *Vindication of the Duke of Guise*, and the *Secular Masque* have half-titles with the imprint 'Printed in the YEAR M DCC XVII.' with the following exceptions: the *Essay of Dramatic Poesie* has no imprint; *Troilus and Cressida*, *Spanish Friar*, *Duke of Guise*, the *Vindication*, *Albion and Albanius*, *Amphitryon*, *King Arthur*, and *Love Triumphant* read 'Year'; *Albion and Albanius* precedes the imprint with '*LONDON:*' | ; the imprint for *Don Sebastian* reads: '*LONDON:* | Printed for *Benjamin Tooke* and *George Strahan*. 1717.'; the imprint for the *Dialogue and Secular Masque* reads: 'LONDON: | Printed for *Benjamin Tooke* at the *Middle-Temple* | Gate in *Fleet-Street*. M DCC XVII.' All plays, *Essay of Dramatic Poesie*, *Vindication of the Duke of Guise*, *Essay of Heroick Plays*, *Defence of the Epilogue*, *Apology for Heroic Poetry*, and the *Life of Cleomenes* have head-titles. The general title in the Hodges copy (*vol. 1*, A2) is a cancellans. The portrait of Dryden which opens each volume is signed on the right '*Vertue S.*' The engraved surface measures 128 x 75 mm. *Limberham* on the volume 4 title page is spelled 'LIMRERHAM' and *Aureng-Zebe* '*AURENGE-ZEBE*'; *Albanius* on volume 5 title page is spelled 'ALBIANUS.' Congreve wrote the dedicatory epistle to Newcastle; Macdonald speculates that he gave some supervision to the edition. Macdonald 109 a i.

PR3412 .C6 1717

## 94. 1718

[General title in vol. 1 only] as in 1717 (93.) except for | Printed for *J. Tonfon:* And Sold by *J. Bro-* | *therton* and *W. Meadows* at the Black | Bull in *Cornhill*. M DCC XVIII.

[*vol. titles*] as in 1717 (93.)

*Collation:* 12°. *vol. 1: A*² a¹² A³-A¹² B-M¹² N¹²(-N7 + NO¹²) O-P¹² Q⁶; *vol. 2:* A-S¹² T6; *vol. 4:* A-T¹²; *vol. 5:* A-R¹²; *vol. 6:* A-X¹²Y⁴.

*Signing and numbering:* as in 1717 (93.) except that the following pagination errors are corrected: *vol. 4*, 298, 310; *vol. 6*, 323. Volume 2, G4, is missigned as C4.

*Note:* Another issue. The volume title of the first volume now follows the dedication. Volume 3 of the Hodges set, although bound to conform to the other volumes, is not a part of this issue, but is a duplicate of volume 3 of the 1725 edition. Each volume has the signature 'Geo. Gibson 1794'. Macdonald 109 a ii.

PR3412 .C6 1718

## 95. 1725

[General title in vol. 1 only] as in 1717 (93.) except for | Printed for JACOB TONSON at *Shake-* | *ſpear's Head* in the *Strand.* | [partial rule] M DCC XXV.

[*vol. titles*] *vol. 1:* [as in 1717 (93.) except for | Printed in the YEAR M DCC XXV.] *vol. 2–6:* [as in 1717 (93.) except for imprint date, *Head*, (with comma) in vols. 2, 4, 5, 6; vol. 6 has some rearrangement of type of the play titles and separates them by a double vertical rule.]

*Collation:* 12°. *vol. 1: A² *A³-*A¹² A³-A¹² B-Q¹²R⁶, pp. 1–4 [20] 5–15* 16–83 *84–93* 94–164 *165–183* 184–248 *249–253* 254–293 *294–329* 330–394 *395–396; vol. 2:* [as in *vol. 2,* 93.] *vol. 3:* A-S¹²T⁶, pp. *1–29,* 30–92 *93–97* 98–172 *173–199* 200–280 *281–295* 296–368 *369–381* 382–442 *443–444; vol. 4:* [as in *vol. 4,* 93.] *vol. 5:* [as in *vol. 5,* 93.] *vol. 6:* A-X¹²Y⁴, pp. *1–6* 7–25 *26* 27–142 *143–144* 145–151 *152* 153–231 *232–234* 235–281 *282* 283–350 *351–352* 353–361 *362* 363–409 *410–412* 413–419 *420* 421–499 *500–502* 503–511 *512.*

*Contents: vol. 1: A1* blank; *A1ᵛ* Dryden portrait; *A2:* general title (verso blank); *A3 dedicatory epistle; A3 vol. title (verso blank); A4 *Essay of Dramatic Poesie* half-title (verso blank); A5 dedicatory epistle; A7ᵛ address to the reader; A8 *Essay* text; D6ᵛ blank; D7 *Wild Gallant* half-title (verso blank); D8 preface; D9 original prologue; D10 prologue at revival; D10ᵛ dramatis personae; D11 *WG* text; G11 original epilogue; G11ᵛ epilogue at revival; G12ᵛ blank; H1 *Rival Ladies* half-title (verso blank); H2 dedicatory epistle; H7 prologue; H7ᵛ dramatis personae; H8 *RL* text; L5 *Indian Queen* half-title (verso blank); L6 prologue; L6ᵛ dramatis personae; L7 *IQ* text; N3ᵛ epilogue; N4 *Indian Emperor* half-title (verso blank); N5 dedicatory epistle; N7ᵛ blank; N8 *Defence of an Essay;* O6ᵛ statement of connection; O7ᵛ prologue; O8ᵛ dramatis personae; O9 *IE* text; R6 epilogue; R6ᵛ blank.
*vol. 2:* [as in 93.]
*vol. 3: A1ᵛ* Dryden portrait; A2 vol. title (verso blank); A3 *Conquest of Granada Part I;* D12 *Conquest Part II;* H3ᵛ *Defence of the Epilogue;* H11 *Marriage a la Mode;* M10 *The Assignation;* Q6 *Amboyna.*
*vol. 4:* [as in 93.]

*vol. 5:* [as in 93.]

*vol. 6:* [as in 93. except that Y4ᵛ is blank]

RT] *vol. 1: DEDICATION.* \*A3ᵛ-\*A12ᵛ; *The Epiſtle Dedicatory.* A5ᵛ-A7; *An* Essay *of Dramatick Poeſie.* A8ᵛ-D6; *The* WILD GALLANT. D11ᵛ-G10ᵛ; *The Epiſtle Dedicatory.* H2ᵛ-H6ᵛ; *The* RIVAL LADIES. H8ᵛ-L4ᵛ; *The* INDIAN QUEEN. L7ᵛ-N3; *The Epiſtle Dedicatory.* N5ᵛ-N7; *Defence of an Eſſay | of Dramatick Poeſie.* N8ᵛ-06; *The* INDIAN EMPEROR. O9ᵛ-R5ᵛ [EMPEROUR. P11]

*Note:* Each play in vols. 2–6 has separate running-title as above.

CW] *vol. 1:* \*A11ᵛ he D6 THE [D6ᵛ blank] F3 *Boy:* [*Boy.*] I6 *Hippolito,* [*Hippolito*] L2ᵛ *Cap.* [*Capt.*] L8ᵛ *Mont,* [*Mont*] N7 A[N7ᵛ blank] N9 what [*what*] Q10 *Aiib.* [*Alib.*] Q12ᵛ *Chr. Pr.* [no cw on C9, C9ᵛ, I12, L7]

*Signing and numbering:* $5 signed (-*vol. 1,* R4.5; *vol. 2,* T4.5; *vol. 3,* E5, T4.5; *vol. 6,* Y3.4; + *vol. 1,* L6; *vol. 4,* M6). On $1 of each signed gathering (plus *vol. 1,* sig. H2) in signature-line next fold 'VOL. I.' and according to volume with rom. numbers. Press figures are present as follows: *vol. 1:* \*A6ᵛ-6, A8ᵛ-5, B12ᵛ-3, C11ᵛ-8, C12ᵛ-8, D8-5, E7-2, F12-4, G5ᵛ-4, H12ᵛ-5, I4ᵛ-4, K11-3, L11ᵛ-4, M8-5, N6ᵛ-8, O12-1; *vol. 2:* A7-4, B12ᵛ-5, C7-5, D11ᵛ-4, F2ᵛ-4, F7ᵛ-1, G7-2, H12-4, I6ᵛ-4, K6ᵛ-2, L6-1, L12ᵛ-8, M11-8, M11ᵛ-8, N7ᵛ-5, O11-6, P12-5, Q12-6, R11ᵛ-6, S6-1, T6-1; *vol. 3:* A6-1, A6ᵛ-6, B7ᵛ-1, C6-6, C7-1, D8-1, E7ᵛ-1, E12ᵛ-6, F12-1, G12-6, H12-1, I12-6, K11ᵛ-1, L7-6, L11ᵛ-1, M5ᵛ-6, N12-8, N12ᵛ-8, O12-4, O12ᵛ-8, P1ᵛ-8, P2ᵛ-8, R11ᵛ-6, S8-1; *vol. 4:* A8ᵛ-1, B12-5, D1ᵛ-4, E6ᵛ-6, F2ᵛ-8, F12-8, G11ᵛ-6, H8ᵛ-5, M7-6, N12-8, N12ᵛ-8, O1ᵛ-4, P8ᵛ-1, R8-6, T2ᵛ-6; *vol. 5:* A8ᵛ-8, A11ᵛ-6, B12ᵛ-3, C5ᵛ-8, C7-5, E11-6, F5ᵛ-8, I8-6, K12-4, L11ᵛ-5, M7ᵛ-4, N2ᵛ-4, O11-6, O11ᵛ-5, R8ᵛ-1; *vol. 6:* A8-3, A8ᵛ-3, B5ᵛ-2, B12ᵛ-3, C12ᵛ-3, D12ᵛ-3, E8ᵛ-2, E11ᵛ-3, F2ᵛ-3, F8-2, G7ᵛ-3, G8ᵛ-2, H11ᵛ-2, H12ᵛ-2, I7-3, I8-2, K5ᵛ-1?, K6ᵛ-1, L5ᵛ-2, L7-2, M2ᵛ-1, M12-3, N11-3, O5ᵛ-1, O12ᵛ-2, P11ᵛ-1, P12ᵛ-1, Q6ᵛ-1, Q11ᵛ-2, R6-1, R8ᵛ-3, S8-2, S12ᵛ-1, T6-2, T7-3, U11-3, X5ᵛ-3, X7-3, Y2ᵛ-2. Following errors in pagination: *vol. 1:* 346 misnumbered as 246; *vol. 2:* 350 as 035; *vol. 3:* 79 as 59, 170 as 171, 171 as 172, 313 as 213, 321 as 325, 324 as 238, 325 as 329, 328 as 342, 333 as 337, 368 as 364; *vol. 4:* 328 as 38, 376 as 76; *vol. 5:* 323 as 223, 341 as 331, 380 as 404, 398 as 498; *vol. 6:* 54 as 55, 55 as 54, 315 as 135, 427 as 327; 386 has the figures reversed and the last two inverted.

*Type:* text (*vol. 1,* E2): 38ll., 122(130) x 72 mm., 64 R.

*Notes:* A reprint, largely paginal with different ornaments, of 93. Congreve's dedication to Newcastle has been reset in twenty pages; a cancellans for N7, vol. 1. of 93. (O7, vol. 1, of this edition) has been filled by spreading the explanation of the connection between the *Indian Queen* and the *Indian Emperor* and the prologue to the *Indian Emperor* to two pages each. The A, G, and H gatherings of vol. 3 are not paginal reprints of 93. There are two leaf stubs between M5-M6, vol. 4., one between A2-A3, vol. 6, and one between A11-A12, vol. 6. All plays, the *Essay of Dramatic Poesie*, the *Vindication of the Duke of Guise*, and the *Secular Masque* have half-titles with the imprint 'Printed in the YEAR M DCC XXV.' with the following exceptions: the *Essay of Dramatic Poesie* has no imprint; 'Year' replaces 'YEAR' in the imprint of *Troilus, Spanish Friar, Don Sebastian, Amphitryon, Cleomenes, King Arthur,* and *Love Triumphant;* the date on *Cleomenes, King Arthur, Don Sebastian,* and *Love Triumphant* is given as 'M.DCC.XXV.'; the imprint on *Albion and Albanius* and *Don Sebastian* is preceded by '*LONDON:*'; the imprint on *Limberham* and *Oedipus* reads '*LONDON:* | Printed for M. POULSON. 1725.'; on the *Duke of Guise:* '*LONDON:* | Printed for J. TONSON, and | M. POULSON. 1725.'; on *Dialogue:* '*LONDON:* | Printed for *B. Motte,* M.DCC.XXV.' The selections have head-titles as in 93. Each volume contains the Vertue portrait of Dryden. Macdonald 109b.

PR3412 .C6 1725

## 96. 1762

[General title in vol. 1 only] THE DRAMATICK | WORKS | OF *l* JOHN DRYDEN, EſQ. | IN | SIX VOLUMES. | [device: T1] ||| LONDON: | Printed for J. and R. TONSON in the Strand. | [partial rule] M DCC LXII.

*[vol. titles] vol. 1:* THE DRAMATICK | WORKS | OF | JOHN DRYDEN, EſQ. | VOLUME *the* FIRST. | CONTAINING, | An ESSAY of DRAMATICK POESY. | The WILD GALLANT. | The RIVAL LADIES. | The INDIAN QUEEN. | The INDIAN EMPEROR: | Or, the Conqueſt of MEXICO. ||| [imprint as on general title]

*vols. 2–6:* [as on vol. 1 except for vol. no. and contents in six to ten lines and imprint date of 'M DCC LXIII.' on vols. 3–5; *Albanius* is misspelled *Albianus* on vol. 5 t-p.]

*Collation:* 12°. *vol. 1:* A¹² a-c¹² B-D¹² E⁶ F-H¹²I⁶ K-P¹², pp. *i–xxix* xxx–xcvi *1–11* 12–82 *83–101* 102–167 *168–175* 176–215 *216–249* 250–311 *312; vol. 2:* A-C¹² D⁶ E-G¹² H⁶ I-U¹²X⁶, pp. *1–15* 16–81 *82–91* 92–166 *167–179* 180–262 *263–295* 296–381 *382–401* 402–465 *466–468; vol. 3:* A-T¹², pp. *1–31* 32–94 *95–103* 104–177 *178–205* 206–286 *287–309* 310–382 *383–395* 396–456; *vol. 4:* A-L¹² M⁶ N-U¹², pp. *1–29* 30–71 *72–91* 92–167 *168–199* 200–275 *276–289* 290–371 *372–383* 384–466 *467–468; vol. 5:* A-R¹², pp. *1–41* 42–119 *120–135* 136–215 *216–231* 232–305 *306–311*

312–360 *361–377* 378 *379* 380–407 *408; vol. 6:* A-N¹² O⁶ P-Q¹² R⁶ S-X¹², pp. *1–27* 28–141 *142–161* 162–238 *239–257* 258–323 *324–339* 340–383 *384–401* 402–477 *478–480*.

*Contents: vol. 1:* A1 title (verso blank); A2 blank; A2ᵛ Dryden portrait; A3 vol. title (verso blank); A4 dedicatory epistle; A11 *Essay of Dramatic Poesy* half-title (verso blank); A12 dedicatory epistle; a2ᵛ address to the reader; a3 *Essay* text; B1 blank; B1ᵛ engraving; B2 *Wild Gallant* half-title (verso blank); B3 preface; B4 original prologue; B5 prologue at revival; B5ᵛ dramatis personae; B6 *WG* text; on E5ᵛ original epilogue; E6 epilogue at revival; F1 blank; F1ᵛ engraving; F2 *Rival Ladies* half-title (verso blank); F3 dedicatory epistle; F8 prologue; F8ᵛ dramatis personae; F9 *RL* text; I6ᵛ blank; K1 blank; K1ᵛ engraving; K2 *Indian Queen* half-title (verso blank); K3 prologue; K3ᵛ dramatis personae; K4 *IQ* text; L12ᵛ epilogue; M1 blank; M1ᵛ engraving; M2 *Indian Emperor* half-title (verso blank); M3 dedicatory epistle; M5ᵛ *Defence of Essay of Dramatic Poesy;* N3ᵛ statement of connection; N4 prologue; N4ᵛ dramatis personae; N5 *IE* text; P12ᵛ epilogue. *vol. 2:* A1: vol. title (verso blank); A3 *Secret Love;* E2 *Sir Martin Mar-All;* I2 *Tempest;* N2 *Evening's Love;* S2 *Tyrannick Love. vol. 3:* A1: vol. title (verso blank); A3 *Conquest of Granada Part I;* E2 *Conquest of Granada Part II;* H6 *Defence of the Epilogue;* I2 *Marriage a la Mode;* N2 *Assignation;* R2 *Amboyna. vol. 4:* A1 vol. title (verso blank); A3 *State of Innocence;* D2 *Aureng-Zebe;* H2 *All for Love;* N2 *Limberham;* R2 *Oedipus. vol. 5:* A1 vol. title (verso blank); A3 *Troilus and Cressida;* F2 *Spanish Friar;* K2 *Duke of Guise;* N11 *Vindication of the Duke of Guise;* Q2 *Albion and Albanius. vol. 6:* A1 vol. title (verso blank); A3 *Don Sebastian;* G2 *Amphitryon;* L2 *Cleomenes;* P2 *King Arthur;* S2 *Love Triumphant.*

RT] *vol. 1: DEDICATION.* A4ᵛ-A10ᵛ; *The Epiſtle Dedicatory.* A12ᵛ-a2; *An* ESSAY *of Dramatick Poeſy.* a3ᵛ-c12ᵛ; *The* WILD GALLANT. B6ᵛ-E5ᵛ [GALLANT (no period) C10, D10, E5]; *The Epiſtle Dedicatory.* F3ᵛ-F7ᵛ; *The* RIVAL LADIES. F9ᵛ-I12; *The* INDIAN QUEEN. K4ᵛ-L12; *The Epiſtle Dedicatory.* M3ᵛ-M5; *Defence of an Eſſay | of Dramatick Poeſy.* M6ᵛ-N3; *The* INDIAN EMPEROR. N5ᵛ-P12.

*Note:* Each play in vols. 2–6 has separate running-title as above.

CW] *vol. 1:* A12ᵛ I b1ᵛ him; [him:] c7 Election [lection] C9 *Burr:* [*Burr.*] G4ᵛ *Ang.* [*Ang*] G10 *Gonſ.* [*Gon.*] N8 *Alm,* [*Alm.*] O12ᵛ Their [no cw on N8ᵛ]

*Signing and numbering:* $5 signed (*-vol. 1*, E4.5, I4.5; *vol. 2,* D4.5, H4.5, X4.5; *vol. 4,* M4.5; *vol. 6,* O4.5, R4.5). On the first signed leaf of each gathering (except vol. 2, I2; vol. 3, A3; vol. 5, A3; vol. 6, A3, G2, L2, P2, S2; but in addition vol. 2, I3; vol. 3, A4, I3, R3; vol. 4, D3, N3; vol. 5, F3, K3; vol. 6, A4, G3, L3, P3, S3) in the signature line next fold 'VOL. I.' and according to volume with rom. numbers. Press figures are present as follows: *vol. 3:* O2ᵛ-1, P12ᵛ-3; on vol. 5, H12ᵛ is an 'S', which may function as a press figure. Following errors in pagination and signatures: *vol. 1:* H4 missigned as G4; *vol. 2:* I5 missigned as A5; *vol. 3:* I2 missigned as I; p. 119 misnumbered as 911, 136 as 336.

*Type:* text (vol. 1, B9): 40 ll., 133(142) x 73 mm., 67 R.

*Notes:* The first volume includes the Vertue engraving of Dryden; each play is preceded by a Gravelot-Vander Gucht engraving which bears both engraving signatures and the volume and page number which the engraving is to face. Except for the first engraving in each volume, the engravings are pasted on the inside of the cancellandum stub of the first leaf in the gathering: the engraving stub then, as the volumes were bound, appears between the eleventh and twelfth leaves of the gathering (The one exception to this is the N gathering of vol. 3 where the engraving does not seem to be pasted in and where a cancel stub exists between N2 and N3.). Since the first leaf in each volume is the volume title page, the first engraving is pasted to the inside of the stub of the second leaf and the engraving stub falls between A10 and 11. All plays, the *Essay of Dramatic Poesy,* and the *Vindication of the Duke of Guise* have half-titles without imprints; the selections as listed in 93. have head-titles. The *Life of Cleomenes* and *A Dialogue and Secular Masque* are omitted from this edition. Macdonald 109 d.

PR3412 .C6 1762

## *Familiar Letters of Love, Gallantry, and Several Occasions.* 1718

## 97. 1718

[in black and red within double rules] *Familiar Letters* | OF | LOVE, GALLANTRY, | *And several OCCASIONS,* | By the WITS of the laſt and preſent Age. | *VIZ.* |

| | |
|---|---|
| Mr. BUTLER, Author of | Mrs. MANLY. |
|   *HUDIBRASS.* | Mrs. TROTTER. |
| Mr. FLATMAN. | Mrs. CENT LIVRE. |
| Mr. DRYDEN. | Sir _____ _____ |
| Mr. CONGREVE. | Sir R. L'ESTRANGE. |
| Mr. WYCHERLEY. | Sir _____ _____ |
| Mr. DENNIS. | Sir JOHN DENHAM. |
| Mr. FARQUHAR. | Sir GEO. ETHEREGE. |
| Mr. EDW. WARD. | Earl of CLARENDON. |
| Mr. MOYLE. | Earl of DORSET. |
| Mr. OTWAY. | D. of BUCKINGHAM. |
| Mrs. BEHN. | D. of DEVONSHIRE, *&c.* |

From their ORIGINALS. | *With their EFFIGIES Curioufly Engraved by the Beft* Maſters. | Together with | Mr. *T. Brown*'s Remains; | Being LETTERS and DIALOGUES on the | Times, not Printed in his works. || The whole in Two Volumes, Compleat. || *LONDON*, Printed for SAM. BRISCOE. | *R. Smith, G. Strahan, E. Symons, J. Osborne, J. Brotherton,* | at the *Royal Exchange*: *W. Taylor, A. Bettefworth, J.* | *Batley*, in *Pater-nofter-row*: *J. Brown, W. Mears, F. Clay,* | without *Temple-bar*: *J. Barnes, J. Greaves*, in St. | *James*'s; and *J. Morphew* near *Stationers-Hall.* 1718.

*Collation:* 12°. π1A⁴ B-L¹² M⁸, 133 leaves, pp. [10] 1–92 *93* 94–256 [251 misnumbered as 151], plates [4] (opp. sigs. π1, B1, C3, G1), \$5 (-A2-4, M5) signed [missigning E6 as E5].

HT] [orn.: centered medallion of laurel-wreathed head, flaming lamps at sides, within border (18 x 71)] | A | COLLECTION | OF | *LETTERS* | ON | Several Occaſions, *&c.* ||

*Contents:* π1: title (verso blank). A1: [orn. as in HT] | 'TO THE | NOBILITY AND GENTRY | OF | *BRITAIN*.' [orn. initialⁱ]. Signed on A2ᵛ 'SAM. BRISCOE.' A3: [quadruple row of fleurons] | 'THE | CONTENTS | OF THE | Firſt VOLUME of LETTERS.' [orn. initial⁷]. B1: HT with text headed 'Sir *Hudibras*'s EPISTLE to the Widow | BLACKGROVE. || *By Mr.* SAMUEL BUTLER.' || [fact⁴]. On C3: [double row of fleurons] | 'LOVE-LETTERS, | *By Mrs.* A. BEHN, *never before Printed.*' [orn. initialⁱ]. On C11: [row of type orn.] | 'BYBLIS's *paffionate Love-Letter to her* | *Brother. From* Ovid's Metamorphoſis. || *By Mr.* DENNIS.' || [fact⁵]. On D7ᵛ: [double row of type orn.] | 'REFLECTIONS *and* ANNOTATIONS | *on Mr.* OLDHAM. || By the Same.' || [fact⁵]. On D11: 3 other Dennis letters. On E5: [row of type orn.] | 'To his MISTRESS. || *By Sir* JOHN DENHAM.' || [fact⁴]. On E5ᵛ: [row of fleurons] | 'To Mrs. HUNT at *Epfom.* || *By Mr.* CONGREVE.' || [fact⁶] On E6: [row of type orn.] | 'A Letter to WALTER MOYLE, Eſq; | *By* ANTHONY HAMOND, *Efq*; || [fact⁴] On E7: [row of type orn.] 'A SATYR againſt POETRY, in a | LETTER to the Right Honourable | the Earl of *Dorfett.*' [fact⁴] E11: [orn.: rect. of lozenge, wheel, and crown. type orn. enclosing a double row of fleurons (19 x 71)] | 'A | COLLECTION | OF | LETTERS. || *Written by feveral Eminent Hands.* || The FOURTH EDITION.' || below: dedicatory epistle (fact⁷). F2: address to the reader (fact⁵) headed by double row of type orn. F3: [orn.: rect. of lozenge and wheel orn. enclosing double row of fleurons (18 x 71)] | 'A | COLLECTION | OF | *LETTERS, &c.*' || [fact⁵]. K10: [orn.: rect. of lozenge and wheel orn. enclosing double row of fleurons (19 x 71)] | 'MEMOIRS | OF THE | *Fair* ELOISA, *a Nun,* | AND | ABELARD, *a Monk.* || *Tranflated by Sir* ROGER L'ESTRANGE.' || [fact⁵]. On L11ᵛ: other letters.

RT] [varies with contents]

CW] A4ᵛ A B8 Then [Than] B11ᵛ RALPHO'*s* [RALPHO'S] C12ᵛ For D10ᵛ
LYONS, [*A*] E11 when [When] F12ᵛ *Mr.* G12ᵛ laugh H4 *Qui* [*Que*] I12ᵛ and K12ᵛ
caus'd L12ᵛ the [The corners of B6, G6, and M2 have been torn off in the Hodges
copy so that no cw is evident; no cw on M7.]

   *Type:* text (F4): 37 ll., 126(135) x 71 mm., 68 R.

   *Notes:* On B1, G1, H1, I1, K1 in the signature line next fold '[VOL. I.]' and
E1 and F1 '[VOL. II.]'. Each of the verse letters begins with a 4-line fact.; each
of the prose letters with a 5-line fact. The volume title page is preceded by the
Vander Gucht engraving of the Kneller portrait of Congreve. An engraving of
Samuel Butler faces B1; the engraved surface measures 100 x 71 mm. and is
signed on the left '*P. et. Lilly pinx.*' and on the right '*M. Vdr. Gucht Scul.*' An
engraving of Aphra Behn faces C3; the engraved surface measures 100 x 82 and
is signed on the left '*Riley Pinx.*' and on the right '*R. Weſt.*' An engraving of
Wycherly faces G1; the engraved surface measures 104 x 75 mm. and is signed on
the left '*P. Lely Eq. Pinx.*' and on the right '*M. Vdr. Gucht Scul.*' Stubs between
B12-C1, C10-C11, and E12-F1 may be the stubs of other disjunct engravings
which have been removed or they may be binding stubs for the existing
engravings. From E11, the volume is in large part a reprint of the earlier *Letters
upon Several Occasions.* The volume contains four Congreve letters of which only
the letter to Arabella Hunt, dated July 26, 1694 (Hodges, 146) was not printed
in the earlier volume. Bound in brown leather. The Hodges collection contains
only the first volume of the edition. Case 305.

PN6140 .L7F3 v.1

## *Literary Relics.* 1789

## 98. 1789

LITERARY   RELICS: | CONTAINING | ORIGINAL   LETTERS |
FROM | KING CHARLES II. KING JAMES II. | THE QUEEN
OF BOHEMIA, | SWIFT, BERKELEY, ADDISON, STEELE, |
CONGREVE, THE DUKE OF ORMOND, | AND BISHOP
RUNDLE. | To which is prefixed, | AN INQUIRY | INTO | THE
LIFE OF DEAN SWIFT. ‖ BY GEORGE-MONCK BERKELEY,
ESQ; | L.L.B. IN THE UNIVERSITY OF DUBLIN, F.S.S.A. | A
MEMBER OF ST MARY MAGDALEN HALL OXFORD, | AND OF
THE INNER TEMPLE LONDON. ‖ LONDON: | PRINTED FOR
C. ELLIOT and T. KAY, No 332. Strand; | And C. ELLIOT Parliament
Square,  Edinburgh. | M,DCC,LXXXIX.

*Half-title:* [row of type orn.] | LITERARY RELICS. | [row of type orn.] | 1789.

*Collation:* 8°. a⁴ b-d⁸ A-2C⁸, 236 leaves, pp. *i–vii* viii–xii *xiii* xiv–lvi *1* 2–415 *416* [120 misprinting as 210], $4 (-E4; +D5) signed [misprinting F3 as F2]

*Contents: a1:* half-title (verso blank). *a2:* title (verso blank). *a3:* 'TO THE RIGHT HONOURABLE | JOHN MONCK MASON,...' (verso blank). *a4:* ||| 'PREFACE.' b3: ||| 'INQUIRY | INTO THE | LIFE OF DEAN SWIFT.' A1: [partial double rule] | 'ORIGINAL LETTERS | FROM | CHARLES II. JAMES II. AND THE | QUEEN OF BOHEMIA, | TO THE | MARQUIS OF MONTROSE.' B4: ||| 'SWIFT's LETTERS.' E5ᵛ: ||| 'LETTERS of the Rev. Dr | GEORGE BERKELEY, afterwards | Biʃhop of Cloyne.' U7: [partial double rule] | 'LETTERS from Mr WILLIAM | CONGREVE so JOSEPH KEALLY, Eʃq.' 2A8ᵛ: 'LETTERS from JOSEPH ADDISON, | Eʃq; to JOSEPH KEALLY, Eʃq; | of Keally Mount in the county | of Kilkenny.' 2B6: 'LETTERS from Sir RICHARD | STEELE, Knt. to JOSEPH KEAL- | LY, Eʃq; of Keally Mount in the | county of Kilkenny.' 2C1: 'LETTERS from his Grace the | DUKE of ORMOND to JOSEPH | KEALLY, Eʃq; of Keally Mount | in the county of Kilkenny.' 2C3: 'LETTER from the Right Reve- | rend Father in God THOMAS | RUNDLE, Lord Biʃhop of Derry, | to Mr RICHARDSON.' 2C8ᵛ: blank.

RT] INQUIRY INTO THE | LIFE OF DEAN SWIFT. b3ᵛ-d8. LITERARY | RELICS. A1ᵛ-2C8.

CW] c2ᵛ Mrs ["Mrs] c3 however, ["however,] B4 and [myself] E7ᵛ (fire-) ʃide, [ʃide.] K2ᵛ me [your] M3 XXII. [XXXII.] P2ᵛ L. [XLIX.] P5 LIII. [LII.] Q2ᵛ LVIII. [LVI.] T2ᵛ LXXV. [LXXIV.] [no cw on d5ᵛ, K5, Z5, Z7, Z8]

*Type:* text (C2): 25 ll., 139(155) x 81 mm., 112 R.

*Note:* Press figures are present as follows: b8-5, c2ᵛ-4, c7ᵛ-6, d6ᵛ-5, d7ᵛ-4, A2-5, A8ᵛ-1, B6ᵛ-3, B7ᵛ-2, C6-2, D7-5, D8-1, E4ᵛ-5, E7ᵛ-6, F5ᵛ-3, F8ᵛ-4, G5ᵛ-1, G6ᵛ-3, H5ᵛ-3, H8ᵛ-6, I8-6, K6-1, K6ᵛ-5, L5ᵛ-2, L6ᵛ-3, M7-5, M7ᵛ-6, N4ᵛ-6, N5ᵛ-3, O5-1, O6-2, P1ᵛ-6, P8ᵛ-4, Q5ᵛ-2, Q7-3, R7ᵛ-1, R8ᵛ-5, S1ᵛ-6, S2ᵛ-4, T5-5, T6-1, U5-3, U7ᵛ-2, X1ᵛ-6, X7-5, Y7ᵛ-4, Y8ᵛ-6, Z7ᵛ-3, Z8ᵛ-2, 2A7-6, 2A7ᵛ-1, 2B7ᵛ-5, 2B8ᵛ-2, 2C6ᵛ-6, 2C7ᵛ-6. Bound in marbled boards. The 43 letters from Congreve to Joseph Keally are included by Hodges, although Hodges has corrected a number from holographs.

PR1345 .B4

## Collected Poems.

### 99. 1752

POEMS | UPON | SEVERAL  OCCASIONS. | BY | MR.  WILLIAM
CONGREVE. | [2-line motto from Horace and ack.] | GLASGOW, |
PRINTED AND SOLD BY R. AND A. FOULIS | M DCC LII.

*Half-title:* S3: A | PINDARIQUE | ODE, | Humbly offer'd to the |
QUEEN, | On the Victorious Progreſs of | Her MAJESTY's Arms,
under the | Conduct of the Duke of MARLBOROUGH. | To which is
prefix'd, | A DISCOURSE on the PINDARIQUE ODE. | [2-line motto
from Horace and ack.]

*Collation:* 12°. A-2A⁴, 96 leaves, pp. *1–5* 6–139 *140–142* 143–189
*190–192* [39 misnumbered as 93], $2 signed.

*Contents:* A1: title (verso blank). A2: dedicatory epistle (cap²). A3: text of
poems. S3: queen's pindaric ode half-title (verso blank). 2A3ᵛ: table of the
poems. 2A4ᵛ: blank.

RT] POEMS UPON | SEVERAL OCCASIONS. [OCCASIONS (no period)
D1]

*Type:* text (C2): 34 ll., 115(121) x 64 mm., 68 R.

*Notes:* No cw; no press figures. Each poem begins with a 2-line cap. Notes
on the discourse on the pindaric ode and on the address to the reader of 'Homer's
Hymn to Venus' are printed in double columns. The poems follow the order in
the Tonson editions. Bound in brown leather.

PR3364 .P6 1752

## Dramatic Works.

### 100. 1710

[within double rules] FIVE | PLAYS, | Written by | Mr. *CONGREVE.* |
*VIZ.* | [4 lines braced to the right] *The  Old  Batchelor,* | *The*
*Double-Dealer,* | *The Way of the World,* | *Love for Love,* [to the right]
COMEDIES. | *The  Mourning-Bride,*  A  TRAGEDY. || *LONDON:* |
Printed and Sold by *H. Hills,* in *Black-* | *Fryars,* near the *Water-ſide.*
1710.

*Section-titles:* A1: THE | Old Batchelor. | A | COMEDY. | As it is ACTED at the | THEATRE ROYAL, | BY | Her  MAJESTY'S Servants. ‖ Written by Mr. *CONGREVE.* ‖ [4-line motto from Horace and 1-line ack.] ‖ [imprint as on title except for omission of date] ²A1: THE | Double-Dealer. | A | COMEDY. | As it is Acted at the | THEATRE ROYAL. | BY | Their MAJESTY'S Servants. ‖ Written by Mr. *CONGREVE.* ‖ [1-line motto from Horace and 1-line ack.; 4-line motto from Terence and ack.] ‖ [imprint as on title except for omission of date] ³A1: THE | Way of the World. | A | COMEDY. | As it is Acted at the  | THEATRE | In *Lincoln's-Inn-Fields,* | BY| His MAJESTY'S Servants. ‖ Written by Mr. *CONGREVE.* ‖ [3-line motto from Horace and ack.] ‖ [imprint as on title except for omission of date] ⁴A1: *LOVE* for *LOVE.* | A | COMEDY. | ACTED at the | THEATRE | In *Little-Lincoln's-Inn-Fields,* | BY | His MAJESTY'S Servants. ‖ Written by Mr. *CONGREVE.* ‖ [2-line motto from Horace and ack.] ‖ [imprint as on title except for omission of date] ⁵A1: THE | Mourning Bride. | A | TRAGEDY. | As it is ACTED at the | Theatre in *Lincoln's-Inn-Fields,* | BY | His MAJESTY'S Servants. ‖ Written by Mr. *CONGREVE.* ‖ [2-line motto from Ovid and 1-line ack.] ‖ [imprint as on title except for omission of date]

*Collation:* 12°. π1 A-C¹² D⁴ ²A⁸ ²B-²D¹² ³A-³D¹² ⁴A-⁴D¹² ⁴E⁴ ⁵A⁸ ⁵B-⁵C¹², 217 leaves, pp. [2] *1-2* 3-80 [30 misnumbered as 80 (inverted 3)]; *²1-2* 3-87 *88;* *³1-2* 3-94 *95-96;* *⁴1-2* 3-104; *⁵1-2 3 4* 5-64, \$5 (-D3.4, ²A5, ⁴E3.4, ⁵A5) signed.

*Contents:* π1 title (verso blank); A1 *OB* s-t (verso blank); A2 Southerne's commendatory poem (cap²) headed by double rule; on A2ᵛ Marsh's commendatory poem (cap²); on A3 Higgons' commendatory poem (cap²); A3ᵛ anonymous prologue (cap²); A4 prologue (cap²); A4ᵛ dramatis personae (with cast); A5 OB text (cap⁴) with HT; D4ᵛ epilogue (cap²) headed by double rule; ²A1 *D-D* s-t (verso blank); ²A2 Dryden's commendatory poem (cap²) headed by double rule; on ²A3 prologue (cap²); on ²A3ᵛ epilogue (cap²); ²A4ᵛ dramatis personae (with cast); ²A5 DD text (cap⁴) with HT; ²D12ᵛ blank; ³A1 *WW* s-t (verso blank); ³A2 prologue (cap²) headed by double rule; on ³A2ᵛ epilogue (cap²); ³A3ᵛ dramatis personae (with cast); ³A4 *WW* text (cap²) with HT; ³D12 advertisement (verso blank); ⁴A1 *LL* s-t (verso blank); ⁴A2 anonymous prologue (cap²) headed by double rule; ⁴A3 prologue (cap²) headed by double rule; on ⁴A3ᵛ epilogue (cap²); ⁴A4ᵛ dramatis personae (with cast); ⁴A5 *LL* text (cap⁴) with HT; ⁵A1 *MB* s-t (verso blank); ⁵A2 prologue (cap²) headed by double rule; ⁵A3 epilogue (cap²) headed by double rule; ⁵A3ᵛ dramatis personae (with cast); ⁵A4 *MB* text (cap³) with HT.

RT] *The Old Batchelor.* A5ᵛ-D4; *The Double-Dealer.* ²A5ᵛ-²D¹² [*Double Dealer.* ²A7-²A8ᵛ, ²B4, ²B11ʳ⁻ᵛ, ²B12ᵛ, ²C4, ²C11ʳ⁻ᵛ, ²C12ᵛ, ²D4, ²D11ʳ⁻ᵛ]; *The Way of the World.* ³A4ᵛ-³D11ᵛ; *Love for Love.* ⁴A5ᵛ-⁴E4ᵛ; *The Mourning Bride.* ⁵A4ᵛ-⁵C12ᵛ.

CW] A12ᵛ after B11ᵛ [Exit. [[Exit] C8ᵛ ACT. [ACT] ²A2 *Bu* [*But*] ²B6 *Cynt.* [*Cynt*] ²C12ᵛ *Mask.* ³A12ᵛ *Fain.* ³C10 *et.* [*Pet.*] ³C12 (a-)way [away] ⁴A12ᵛ Diſſi- [Diſſimulation,] ⁴B12ᵛ *He* ⁴D12ᵛ mayn't ⁵A12ᵛ The [Th']

*Type:* text (A6ᵛ): 41 ll., 134(142) x 76 mm., 65 R.

*Notes:* As the collation suggests, the plays were apparently printed to be sold separately as well as bound together. A separate edition of *The Old Bachelor* with the general title is in the Hodges collection, (11.) and a separate edition of *The Way of the World* without the general title (79.). The volume does not have the scene divisions of the 1710 Tonson edition of the works. Hills was a notorious pirate (W. J. Cameron, "Henry Hills—Pirate," *Turnbull Library Record,* XIV [1960], 6–11) to whose edition of Congreve's plays the dramatist may have alluded in the preface to the 1710 *Works.*

PR3362 .H5 1710

## 101.  1712

FIVE | PLAYS | WRITTEN BY | Mr. *CONGREVE.* | *VIZ.* | [3 lines braced to right and left] *The* OLD BATCHELOR. | *The* MOURNING | BRIDE. | LOVE *for* LOVE. | DOUBLE DEALER. | WAY *of the* WORLD. | [orn. (imitation of T15)] | *LONDON,* | Printed: And Sold by *William Taylor* at the | *Ship* in *Pater-noſter-Row.* 1712.

*Half-title:* π1: || Mr. *CONGREVE's* | PLAYS. ||

*Section-titles:* as in 1710 (100.) except for THE | *OLD BATCHELOR.* [15 lines] || *LONDON:* | Printed in the YEAR 1712.

*Collation:* 12°. π²A¹² (±A 2.3.4) B-C¹²D⁴; ²A⁸ ²B-²C¹²; ³A-³D¹² ³E⁴; ⁴A⁸ ⁴B-⁴D¹²; ⁵A-⁵D¹². $5 (-D3.4, ²A5, ³E3.4, ⁴A5) signed.

*Notes:* A new issue of the Hills' edition with the plays arranged in the follow- ing order: *OB, MB, LL, DD, WW.* Cancellans A2-4 replace the cancellandum, the stubs of which remain. The title and the *OB* section-title have been reset and the half-title added. Bound in brown leather with marbled inset. Two of the variant cw in 1710 —²A2 *Bu* [*But*], ³C10 *et.* [*Pet.*]— seem to be the results of a failure to print. The ornament on the title page is a skilful imitation of Tonson's ornament 15.

PR3362 .T3 1712

## 102. 1733

THE | DRAMATICK WORKS | OF | *WILLIAM CONGREVE*, Eſq; | VIZ. | I. The OLD BATCHELOR. | II. The DOUBLE-DEALER. | III. LOVE FOR LOVE. | IV. The MOURNING BRIDE. | V. The WAY of the WORLD. || *LONDON*, | Printed for W. FEALES at *Rowe*'s Head, the | Corner of *Eſſex-Street*, in the *Strand*. 1733. | Where may be had, juſt printed in Neat Pocket | Volumes, | *Rowe*'s Plays and Poems, in 3 Volumes, 12 mo. | *Steele*'s Four Plays. | *Ben Johnſon*'s Three Plays; and a Catalogue | to 1732. | Lord *Lanſdowne*'s Four Plays, in 12 mo. | And all Sorts of Plays.

*Section-titles:* A2: THE | OLD BATCHELOR. | A | COMEDY. || Written by Mr. CONGREVE. || [4-line motto from Horace and ack.] || [device T1] || *LONDON:* | Printed for J. TONSON: And Sold by W. FEALES, | at *Rowe*'s Head, the Corner of *Eſſex-Street*, in | the *Strand*. MDCCXXXIII. ²A2: THE | DOUBLE DEALER. | A | COMEDY. || Written by Mr. *CONGREVE*. || [device and imprint as on *OB* s-t] ³A2: LOVE *for* LOVE. | A | COMEDY. || [2-line motto from Horace and ack.] || Written by Mr. *CONGREVE*. || [device and imprint as on *OB* s-t] ⁴A2 THE | *MOURNING BRIDE*. | A | TRAGEDY. || Written by Mr. CONGREVE. || [2-line motto from Ovid and 1-line ack.] || [orn. T25] || *LONDON:* | Printed for J. TONSON: And Sold by W. FEALES | at *Rowe*'s Head, the Corner of *Eſſex-Street* | in the *Strand*. 1733. ⁵A2: THE | WAY of the WORLD. |A | COMEDY. || Written by Mr. *CONGREVE*. || [3-line motto from Horace and ack.] || [device and imprint as on *OB* s-t]

*Collation:* 12°. π² A-C¹² D⁶; ²A-²D¹²; ³A-³D¹² ³E⁶; ⁴A-⁴C¹² ⁴D⁶; ⁵A-⁵D¹², 236 leaves, pp. [4] *1–15* 16–84; ²*1–17* 18–94 *95–96*; ³*1–11* 12–106 *107–108*; ⁴*1–13* 14–82 *83–84*; [12] ⁵*1* 2–82 *83–84*. \$5 (-D4.5, ³E4.5, ⁴A5, ⁴D4.5) signed.

*Contents:* π1 blank; π1ᵛ frontispiece; π2 title; π2ᵛ advertisement for *The English Theatre;* A1 blank; A1ᵛ *OB* engraved illustration; A2 *OB* s-t (verso blank); A3 dedicatory epistle (fact⁶) headed by orn. (T2); A4ᵛ Southerne's commendatory poem; on A5 Marsh's commendatory poem; on A5ᵛ Higgons' commendatory poem; A6 Falkland's prologue; on A6$^v$ prologue; on A7 orn. (T4); A7$^v$ dramatis personae (with cast); A8 *OB* text (fact[7]) headed by orn. (T3) and HT; on D6$^v$ epilogue; $^2$A1 blank; $^2$A1$^v$ *DD* engraved illustration; $^2$A2 *DD* s-t (verso blank); $^2$A3 dedicatory epistle (fact[6]) headed by orn. (T2); $^2$A6 Dryden's commendatory poem; on $^2$A7 orn. (T60); $^2$A7$^v$ prologue; on $^2$A8 orn. (T12); $^2$A8$^v$ dramatis personae (with cast); $^2$A9 *DD* text (orn. initial[6]) headed by orn. (T61) and HT; on $^2$D11$^v$ orn. (T60); $^2$D12 epilogue; on $^2$D12$^v$ orn. (T62); $^3$A1 blank; $^3$A1$^v$ *LL* engraved illustration; $^3$A2 *LL* s-t (verso blank); $^3$A3 dedicatory epistle (orn. initial[7]) headed by orn. (T50); $^3$A4$^v$ prologue; on $^3$A5 orn. (T58); $^3$A5$^v$ dramatis personae (with cast); $^3$A6 *LL* text (fact[6]) headed by orn. (T2) and HT; $^3$E6 epilogue; on $^3$E6$^v$ orn. (T62); $^4$A1 blank; $^4$A1$^v$ *MB* engraved illustration; $^4$A2 *MB* s-t (verso blank); $^4$A3 dedicatory epistle (fact[6]) headed by orn. (T36); $^4$A5 blank; $^4$A5$^v$ prologue; $^4$A6$^v$ dramatis personae (with cast); $^4$A7 *MB* text (orn. initial[6]) headed by orn. (T43) and HT; on $^4$D5$^v$ orn. (T60); $^4$D6 epilogue; on $^4$D6$^v$ orn. (T38); $^5$A1 blank; $^5$A1$^v$ *WW* engraved illustration; $^5$A2 *WW* s-t (verso blank); $^5$A3 dedicatory epistle (fact[6]) headed by orn. (T63); $^5$A5 Steele's commendatory poem; $^5$A6 prologue; on $^5$A6$^v$ dramatis personae (with cast); $^5$A7 *WW* text (fact[7]) headed by orn. (T2) and HT; on $^5$D11$^v$ orn. (T12); $^5$D12 epilogue; on $^5$D12$^v$ orn. (T60).

RT] *The* OLD BATCHELOR. A8$^v$-D6$^v$; *The* DOUBLE-DEALER. $^2$A9$^v$-$^2$D11$^v$; LOVE *for* LOVE. $^3$A6$^v$-$^3$E5$^v$; *The* MOURNING BRIDE. $^4$A7$^v$-$^4$D5$^v$ [BRIDE (no period) $^4$B8$^v$, $^4$D4]; *The* WAY *of the* WORLD. $^5$A7$^v$-$^5$D11$^v$ [WORLD (no period) $^5$A12, $^5$C2$^v$]

CW] A7$^v$ THE D2 *Setter*. [*Setter:*] $^2$A8 DRA-[Dramatis] $^2$B12$^v$ Face $^3$B5$^v$ (Inheri-) tane; [tance;] $^5$A3 movin [moving] $^5$D4$^v$ *Min* [*Minc.*] $^5$D10 [*Mira. [Mira.* (no bracket)] [no cw on $^5$A5]

*Type and ornaments:* text (A9): 41 ll., 132(142) x 73 mm., 64 R. The frontispiece ($\pi$1$^v$) is an engraving of the Kneller portrait of Congreve and is signed '*M. V$^{dr}$· Gucht Sculp.*' The engraved surface measures 97 x 74 mm. The *OB* engraved illustration (A1$^v$) depicts the scene (IV, 6) in which Laetitia and Bellmour convince Fondlewife of her fidelity and is signed '*G V$^{dr}$ Gucht. Inv. et Sc.*' The engraved surface measures 131 x 73 mm. The *DD* engraved illustration ($^2$A1$^v$) depicts the dagger scene (V, 17) and is signed '*G. Vander Gucht inv & sculp*'. The engraved surface measures 135 x 78 mm. The *LL* engraved illustration ($^3$A1$^v$) depicts the scene (III, 3) in which Mrs. Frail casts her net for Ben and is signed '*G. Vander Gucht inv & scul*'. The engraved surface measures 131 x 74 mm. The *MB* engraved illustration ($^4$A1$^v$) depicts the scene (II, 6) in which Osmyn, ascending from the tomb, confronts Almeria and Leonora and is signed '*G Vdr Gucht Inv. et Sculp.*' The engraved surface measures 135 x 74 mm. The *WW* engraved illustration ($^5$A1$^v$) depicts the scene (IV, 2) in which Sir Wilful appears before the ladies drunk and is signed '*G Vdr Gucht Inv. et Sc.*' The engraved surface measures 130 x 73 mm. The ornament (T2) on $^2$A3 printed imperfectly as it did on 25.; the headpiece on $^3$A3 (T50) has a broken corner. Southerne's, Dryden's, and Steele's commendatory poems, the prologues (except the prologues to *OB* and *WW*) and the epilogues (except the epilogue to *OB*) are headed by an ornament. Each of the commendatory poems, prologues, and epilogues begins with a 2-line capital. *MB* begins each act with either a factotum or ornamental initial, and only *MB* has rules to separate the scenes.

*Notes:* Press figures are present as follows: B6^v-5; B8-4; ²B7-4; ²D11-1; ³B8^v-4; ³D12-4; ⁴B11-5; ⁵A8-4; ⁵D7^v-4. The Horatian motto on *OB* section title reads *'Spectator,'* [comma]. Three of the plays of this edition, *OB, DD, WW* are present in separate form in the Hodges collection (see 12., 25., 80.). Between ³C12 and ³D1 and between ⁴B12 and ⁴C1 in this copy are 3 cancel stubs. For another binding of this issue of *MB* see 58.

PR3362 .F4 1733

## 103. 1735

[in   black   and   red]   *vol.   1:*   PLAYS | Written   by | *WILLIAM   CONGREVE,* E{q; | In   TWO   VOLUMES. || VOLUME *the* FIRST. || [orn. T24] ||| *LONDON:* | Printed for J. TONSON in the *Strand.* | [half rule] | M DCC XXXV. *vol. 2:* as in vol. 1 except for omission of 'In TWO VOLUMES', a different ornament (T41) and colon after *'LONDON'* not italicized.

*Half-title: vol. 1:* [orn. T64] | VOL. I. | CONTAINING, | [2 lines braced to right] *The* OLD BATCHELOR. | *The* DOUBLE DEALER. [to the right] Comedies. | [orn. T65] *vol. 2* [as in vol. 1 except for different ornaments (T66, 67) and contents list]

*Section-titles: vol. 1:* A2: THE | OLD BATCHELOR. | A | COMEDY. || Written by Mr. *CONGREVE.* || [4-line motto from Horace and ack.] || [device T1] || *LONDON,* | Printed for JACOB TONSON, in the *Strand.* | M DCC XXXV. ²A2: THE | DOUBLE-DEALER. | A | COMEDY. || Written by Mr. *CONGREVE.* || [device T1] ||| *LONDON:* | *Printed for* JACOB TONSON *in the Strand.* | [partial rule] | M DCC XXXV. *vol. 2:* A2: LOVE *for* LOVE. [partly cropped] | A | COMEDY. || [2-line motto from Horace and ack.] || By the Late | Mr. CONGREVE. || [device T1] || [Imprint as on *OB* s-t except for *LONDON:* | ... TONSON [no   comma]   ...   M DCC XXXV (no   period)] ²A2: THE | MOURNING   BRIDE. | A | TRAGEDY. | Written   by | *Mr.* CONGREVE. || [2-line motto from Ovid and 1-line ack.] || [device and imprint as on *DD* s-t] ³A2: THE | WAY of the WORLD. | A | COMEDY. | Written by | *Mr.* CONGREVE. ‖ [3-line motto from Horace and ack.] ‖ [device and imprint as on *MB* s-t]

*Collation:* 12°. *vol. 1:* π³ A-D¹² E⁶ ²A-²D¹² ²E⁶, 111 leaves, pp. [6] *1–15* 16–106 *107–108;* ²*1–15* 16–107 *108; vol. 2:* π² A-E¹² F⁶ ²A-²C¹² ²D⁶ ³A-³E¹², χ¹, 171 leaves, pp. [4] *1–11* 12–32 *33* 34–55 *56* 57–82 *83* 84–109 *110* 111–130 *131–132* [21 misprinting as ζ1 (2 upside-down)]; ²*1–11* 12–82 *83–84;* ³*1–17* 18–116 *117–118* [4], \$5(-*vol. 1:* E4.5, ²A5, ²E4.5 *vol. 2:* F4.5, ²A4.5, ²D4.5; + *vol. 1:* A6, B6, C6, D6; *vol. 2:* A6, B6, C6, D6, E6)

*Contents: vol 1:* π1ʳ⁻ᵛ blank; π2 title (verso blank); π3 half-title (verso blank); A1 blank; A1ᵛ engraving; A2 *OB* s-t (verso blank); A3 dedicatory epistle (fact⁶) headed by orn. (T5); A4ᵛ Southerne's commendatory poem; on A5 Marsh's commendatory poem; on A5ᵛ Higgons' commendatory poem; on A6 Falkland's prologue; A7 prologue; A7ᵛ dramatis personae (with cast); A8 *OB* text (orn. initial⁶) headed by orn. (T6) and HT; on E5ᵛ orn. (T68); E6 epilogue; on E6ᵛ orn. (T7); ²A1 blank; ²A1ᵛ engraving; ²A2 *DD* s-t (verso blank); ²A3 dedicatory epistle (fact⁶) headed by orn. (T69); ²A5ᵛ Dryden's commendatory verses; on ²A6ᵛ orn. (T12); ²A7 prologue; ²A7ᵛ dramatis personae (with cast); ²A8 *DD* text (fact⁶) headed by orn. (T46) and HT; ²E6ᵛ epilogue. *vol. 2:* π1 vol. title (verso blank); π2 half-title (verso blank); A1 blank; A1ᵛ engraving; A2 *LL* s-t (verso blank); A3 dedicatory epistle (fact⁵) headed by orn. (T70); A4ᵛ prologue; on A5 orn. (T71); A5ᵛ dramatis personae (with cast); A6 *LL* text (fact⁶) headed by orn. (T12) and HT; on F5ᵛ orn. (T73); F6 epilogue; on F6ᵛ orn. (T74); ²A1 blank; ²A1ᵛ engraving; ²A2 *MB* s-t (verso blank); ²A3 dedicatory epistle (fact⁶) headed by orn. (T43); ²A4ᵛ prologue; on ²A5 orn. (fleuron type); ²A5ᵛ dramatis personae (with cast); ²A6 *MB* text (orn. initial⁶) headed by orn. (T34) and HT; on ²D5ᵛ orn. (T12); ²D6 epilogue (verso blank); ³A1 blank; ³A1ᵛ engraving; ³A2 *WW* s-t (verso blank); ³A3 dedicatory epistle (orn. initial⁴) headed by orn. (T36); ³A6ᵛ Steele's commendatory poem; ³A7ᵛ prologue; on ³A8 orn. (T29); ³A8ᵛ dramatis personae (with cast); ³A9 *WW* text (orn. initial⁶) headed by orn. (T46) and HT; ³E11 epilogue; on ³E11ᵛ orn. (T60); ³E12ʳ⁻ᵛ blank; χ1ʳ⁻ᵛ blank.

RT] *vol. 1: The* OLD BATCHELOR. A8ᵛ-E5ᵛ [BATDHELOR. D8]; *The* DOUBLE-DEALER. ²A8ᵛ-²E6 [DOUBLE DEALER. (no hyphen) ²A9, ²B6ᵛ, ²C4, ²D6ᵛ]; *vol. 2:* LOVE *for* LOVE. A6ᵛ-F5ᵛ [. . . LOVE : A9ᵛ, C10ᵛ, E10ᵛ; . . . LOVE, B10ᵛ, C1ᵛ, D10ᵛ, E1ᵛ] *The* MOURNING BRIDE. ²A6ᵛ-²D5ᵛ; *The* WAY *of the* WORLD. ³A9ᵛ-³E10ᵛ.

CW] *vol. 1:* A7ᵛ THE B12ᵛ SCENE C12ᵛ *Belin.* D1 But [but,] D3 *Fond.* [*Ford.*] ²A7ᵛ THE ²B12ᵛ SCENE ²C12ᵛ *Brisk.* ²D4 CENE [SCENE] *vol. 2:* A6 *Jer.* [*Jere.*] A9 Work; [work] A12 *Scand.* [*Scan.*] B12ᵛ Mrs. *Fore.* C6ᵛ (Vizor-)

Maʃks [Masks] D4ᵛ *Foa* [*For*] E12ᵛ SCENE ²A5 DRA- [Dramatis] ²B12ᵛ If ²C12ᵛ SCENE ³A8ᵛ THE ³B12ᵛ *Milla.* ³C5ᵛ (*Paʃs-*) *par-toute,* [*par toute,*] ³D12ᵛ with [no cw on *vol. 1,* ²A6; *vol. 2,* A5ᵛ]

*Type and ornaments:* text (vol. 1, A9): 36 ll., 134(143) x 73, 74 R. The engraved illustrations are the Vander Gucht engravings of the Tonson-Feales 1733 edition of the dramatic works. Each commendatory poem, prologue, and epilogue (except the epilogue to the *DD*) is headed by an ornament and each opens with a 2-line cap.; acts and scenes are headed by an ornament; each act of *LL* and *MB* opens with a factotum (5–6 ll.).

*Notes:* Press figures are present as follows: *vol. 1:* A8ᵛ-3, A11ᵛ-2, B7-3, B11ᵛ-2, C7-1, C8-1, D11ᵛ-2, D12ᵛ-2, E4-8, ²D8ᵛ-4; *vol. 2:* A11-5, A11ᵛ-4, B11-6, B12-2, C8-5, C12ᵛ-3, D7ᵛ-2, D8ᵛ-3, E5ᵛ-1, E8ᵛ-2, F1ᵛ-5, ²C12ᵛ-2, ³C11-2, ³D11ᵛ-2, ³E11-2. 2 vols. bound in one. The plays were printed to be sold separately as well as bound together. The Hodges collection contains separate copies of *OB* (13.), *LL* (38.), and *WW* (81.). A copy of the *DD* is bound with other plays (26.).

PR3362 .T6 1735

# 104.  1773

*vol. 1:* THE | DRAMATIC WORKS | OF | WILLIAM CONGREVE, Eʃq; | IN TWO VOLUMES. | VOLUME FIRST. | LONDON: | Printed for S. CROWDER, C. WARE, and T. PAYNE. | M DCC.LXXIII. *vol. 2:* as in vol. 1 except for vol. no. and 'M.DCC.LXXIII.'

*Half-titles: vol. 1,* A3: THE | OLD BACHELOR. | A | COMEDY. || [4-line motto from Horace and 1-line ack. with quotation marks at the beginning of each line.] || The other half-titles follow the same pattern except that *The Double-Dealer* omits a motto.

*Cɔllation: vol. 1:* 12°. π1 A-2C⁶χ1, 158 leaves, pp. [2] *1–6* 7–12 *13–17* 18–96 *97–98* 99–107 *108–111* 112–192 *193–194* 195–197 *198* 199 *200–201* 202–307 *308* 309 *310* [4]; *vol. 2:* π1 A-2A⁶χ1, 146 leaves, pp. [2] *1–7* 8–9 *10* 11 *12–13* 14–75 *76–78* 79–85 *86* 87 *88–89* 90–181 *182–185* 186–190 *191–192* 193 *194–195* 196–218 *219–221* 222–230 *231–233* 234–285 *286* [4].

*Contents: vol. 1:* π1ʳ⁻ᵛ blank; A1 vol. title (verso blank); A2 contents (verso blank); A3 *OB* half-title (verso blank); A4 dedicatory epistle; A5ᵛ Southerne's commendatory poem; on A6 Marsh's commendatory poem; on A6ᵛ Higgons' commendatory poem; B1 Falkland's prologue; B1ᵛ prologue; B2 epilogue; B2ᵛ dramatis personae (with cast); B3 *OB* text (cap³) with HT; I1 *DD* half-title (verso blank); I2 dedicatory epistle; I5 Dryden's commendatory poem; I6ᵛ prologue; K1 epilogue; K1ᵛ dramatis personae (with cast); K2 *DD* text (cap³) with HT; R1 *LL* half-title (verso blank); R2 dedicatory epistle; R3ᵛ prologue; R4ᵛ dramatis personae (with cast); R5 *LL* text (cap³) with HT; 2C4ᵛ epilogue; 2C5ᵛ blank; 2C6ʳ⁻ᵛ blank; χ1ʳ⁻ᵛ blank. *vol. 2:* π1ʳ⁻ᵛ (blank); A1 vol. title (verso blank); A2 contents (verso blank); A3 *MB* half-title (verso blank); A4 dedicatory epistle; A5ᵛ prologue; A6ᵛ dramatis personae (with cast); B1 *MB* text (cap³) with HT; G2ᵛ epilogue; G3 *WW* half-title (verso blank); G4 dedicatory epistle; G6ᵛ Steele's commendatory poem; H1ᵛ prologue; H2ᵛ dramatis personae (with cast); H3 *WW* text (cap³) with HT; Q1ᵛ epilogue; Q2 *Judgment* half-title (verso blank); Q3 *Judgment* text (cap³) with HT; Q6 *Semele* half-title; Q6ᵛ argument; R1ᵛ dramatis personae; R2 *Semele* text (cap²) with HT; T2 *Humour* half-title (verso blank); T3 *Humour* text (cap²) with HT; U2 *Amendments* half-title (verso blank); U3 *Amendments* text (cap²) with HT; 2A5ᵛ blank; 2A6ʳ⁻ᵛ blank: χ1ʳ⁻ᵛ blank.

RT] *vol. 1:* THE OLD BACHELOR. B3ᵛ-H6ᵛ; THE DOUBLE-DEALER. K2ᵛ-Q6ᵛ [DOUBLE DEALER. N²]; LOVE FOR LOVE. R5ᵛ-2C4 [LOVE FOR LGVE. U1]; *vol. 2:* THE MOURNING BRIDE. B1ᵛ-G2; THE WAY OF THE WORLD. H3ᵛ-Q1; THE JUDGMENT OF PARIS. Q3ᵛ-Q5ᵛ; SEMELE. R2ᵛ-T1ᵛ; CONCERNING HUMOUR | IN COMEDY. T3ᵛ-U1; REMARKS ON | Mr COLLIER. U3ᵛ-2A5.

*Signing and numbering:* $3 (-*vol. 1*, A3; *vol. 2*, A3) signed. Half-titles, when they come within the first 3 sheets of the gathering, are signed except for the A gathering in both volumes. The page no. on vol. 2, p. 208, is inverted. On $1 of each signed gathering in signature-line next fold 'VOL. I.' and according to volume with rom. numbers. Press figures are present as follows: *vol. 1:* A6-2, B6ᵛ-2, C6ᵛ-1, D6ᵛ-2, E6ᵛ-1, F6ᵛ-2, G6ᵛ-2, H1ᵛ-2, I5-1, K6ᵛ-2, L6-1, M6ᵛ-2, P4ᵛ-2, Q6-1, R6ᵛ-2, S6ᵛ-2, T6ᵛ-1, U6-2, X6ᵛ-1, Y6ᵛ-2, Z6-1, 2B6-1, 2C4ᵛ-2; *vol. 2:* C6-1, D6ᵛ-1, E6ᵛ-2, G6ᵛ-2, H6ᵛ-1, I6ᵛ-2, K4-1, M6ᵛ-1, N6ᵛ-2, P6-2, S6ᵛ-2, T6ᵛ-2, X6ᵛ-2, Y5ᵛ-1.

*Type:* text (vol. 1, C1): 38 ll., 124(131) x 68 mm., 65 R. Each dedicatory epistle, commendatory poem, prologue, and epilogue begins with a 2-line capital.

*Notes:* This edition follows the scene division of the Tonson *Works*. Act III of *The Double-Dealer* (vol. 1, p. 136) is misnumbered Act II; Scene XXI, Act V, is misnumbered 'XXII.' Scene XV, Act IV, *WW* is misprinted 'V.' The free end-papers have been removed from the front and back of vol. 2. It has no ornaments or catchwords. Bound in brown leather. This is the first edition in the Hodges collection to include the letter on humour and the *Amendments* among the collected works.

PR3360 .D73

## 105.

Another copy

*Notes:* The prefixed and concluding leaves have been removed from volume 1 of this copy. In volume 2 the binder's leaves at front and back have been removed.

PR3360 .D73 cop. 2

## *The Works of William Congreve.*

## 106. 1710

*vol. 1:* THE | FIRST VOLUME | OF THE | WORKS | OF | Mr. *William Congreve;* | CONTAINING, | *The* OLD BATCHELOR. Comedy. | *The* DOUBLE DEALER. Comedy. | LOVE *for* LOVE. Comedy. ‖ ‖ *LONDON:* | Printed for *Jacob Tonſon,* at *Shakeſpear's* Head over-againſt | *Catherine Street* in the *Strand.* M DCC X.

*vols. 2–3:* [as in vol. 1 except for volume number and contents list; the type-setting of the volume line of vol. 2 is slightly smaller than in the other two vols.]

*Section-titles: vol. 1,* A5: THE | *OLD BATCHELOR.* | A | COMEDY. ‖ [4-line motto from Horace plus 1-line ack. ‖ [double row of type orn. centered] ‖ Printed in the Year 1710. K5: THE | *DOUBLE-DEALER.* | A | COMEDY. ‖ [1-line motto from Horace and 1-line ack.; 4-line motto from Terence and ack.] ‖ [double row of fleuron type orn. centered] ‖ Printed in the Year 1710. U7: *LOVE* for *LOVE:* | A | COMEDY. ‖ [2-line motto from Horace and ack.] ‖ [orn. T14] ‖ Printed in the YEAR, 1710. *vol. 2:* A1: THE | *MOURNING BRIDE.* | A | TRAGEDY. ‖ [2-line motto from Ovid and 1-line ack.] ‖ [orn. T15] ‖ Printed in the YEAR 1710. G6: THE | WAY of the WORLD. | A | COMEDY. ‖ [3-line motto from Horace and ack.] ‖ [orn. T14] ‖ Printed in the YEAR 1710. S4: THE | JUDGMENT | OF | *PARIS:* | A | MASQUE. ‖ *Vincis utramque Venus.* Ov. Art. Am. L. I. ‖ [orn. T15] ‖ Printed in the YEAR 1710. T2: *SEMELE.* | AN | OPERA. ‖ *A Natura diſcedimus: Populo nos damus, nullius | rei bono auctori, & in hac re, ſicut in omnibus, | inconſtantiſſimo.* | [to the right] Seneca Ep. 99. ‖ Printed in the YEAR 1710. *vol. 3:* A2: POEMS | UPON | Several Occaſions. ‖ *Minuentur atrae | Carmine curae.* Hor. ‖ [orn. T15] ‖ Printed in the Year 1710.

Collation: 8°. *vol. 1:* π1 A⁸ a⁴ B-2I⁸ χ1, 262 leaves, pp. [26] *1* 2–134 *135–157* 158–298 *299–313* 314–492 [6]; *vol. 2:* π² ᵖA⁴ A-X⁸ χ¹, 175 leaves, pp. [8] *493–507* 508–599 *600–615* 616–771 *772–777*, 778–786 *787–793* 794–832 [= 340] [2] *vol. 3:* A² a² A³-A⁴ B-U⁸, 158 leaves, pp. [12] *833* 834–1069 *1070–1072* 1073–1102 *1103–1104* 1105–1135 *1136* [= 304]

*Contents: vol. 1:* π1ʳ⁻ᵛ blank; A1 vol. title (verso blank); A2 'PREFACE.' (orn. initial³) headed by orn. (T16). A4ᵛ 'ERRATA.'; A5 *OB* section-title (verso blank); A6 dedicatory epistle (orn. initial⁴) headed by orn. (T17); A8 Southerne's commendatory poem (cap³); a1 Marsh's commendatory poem (cap²); on a1ᵛ Higgons' commendatory poem (cap²); a2ᵛ Lord Falkland's prologue (cap³); a3ᵛ prologue (cap²); a4ᵛ dramatis personae (with cast); B1 *OB* text (orn. initial⁵) headed by orn. (T18) and HT; K4 epilogue (cap²); K5 *DD* section-title (verso blank); K6 dedicatory epistle (orn. initial⁴) headed by orn. (T17); L3 Dryden's commendatory poem (cap²); L5 prologue (cap²); L6 dramatis personae (with cast) [verso blank]; L7 *DD* text (orn. initial⁵) headed by orn. (T19) and HT; U6 epilogue (cap²); U7 *LL* section-title (verso blank); U8 dedicatory epistle (orn. initial⁴) headed by orn. (T16); X2 prologue (cap²); on X3: orn. (T20); X3ᵛ epilogue (cap²); X4ᵛ dramatis personae (with cast); X5 *LL* text (orn. initial⁵) headed by orn. (T17) and HT; on 2I6ᵛ orn. (T21); 2I7–8ʳ⁻ᵛ blank; χ1ʳ⁻ᵛ blank. *vol. 2:* π1–π2ʳ⁻ᵛ blank; ᵖA1ʳ⁻ᵛ blank; ᵖA2 vol. title (verso blank) ᵖA3 Steele's commendatory poem (cap²); on ᵖA4ᵛ 'ERRATA.'; A1 *MB* section-title (verso blank); A2 dedicatory epistle (orn. initial⁴) headed by orn. (T17); A4 prologue (cap²); on A5 orn. (T22); A5ᵛ dramatis personae (with cast); A6 *MB* text (orn. initial⁶) headed by orn. (T16) and HT; G4ᵛ epilogue (cap²); on G5 orn. (T23 inverted); G5ᵛ blank; G6 *WW* section-title (verso blank); G7 dedicatory epistle (orn. initial⁵) headed by orn. (T16); H2ᵛ prologue (cap²); H3ᵛ dramatis personae (with cast); H4 *WW* text (orn. initial⁵) headed by quadruple row of type orn. and HT; S2ᵛ epilogue (cap²); S3ᵛ blank; S4 *Judgment* section-title (verso blank); S5 *Judgment* text (orn. initial⁴) headed by orn. (T17) and HT; on T1ᵛ orn. (T22); T2 *Semele* section-title (verso blank); T3 argument (orn. initial⁵) headed by orn. (T16); on T4 orn. (T20); T4ᵛ dramatis personae; T5 *Semele* text (orn. initial⁴) headed by orn. (T17) and HT; χ1ʳ⁻ᵛ blank. *vol. 3:* A1 vol. title (verso blank); A2 *Poems* section-title (verso blank); a1 'EPISTLE | TO THE | RIGHT HONOURABLE | *CHARLES* | Lord *HALIFAX*, &c.' | [44 ll, 'T²O You, my Lord, my Muſe her Tribute pays'] headed by orn. (T16); signed on a2ᵛ '*W. CONGREVE.*' A3 ‖ ‖ 'THE | CONTENTS.'; A4ᵛ 'ERRATA.'; B1: text of the poems (cap²) headed by orn. (T16); Q7ᵛ blank; Q8 queen's pindarique ode half-title (verso blank); S8 *Homer's Hymn* half-title (verso blank); U8ᵛ blank.

RT] *vol. 1. The* OLD BATCHELOR. B1ᵛ-K3ᵛ; *The* DOUBLE-DEALER. L7ᵛ-U5ᵛ; LOVE *for* LOVE. X5ᵛ-2I6ᵛ. *vol. 2. The* MOURNING BRIDE. A6ᵛ-G4; *The* WAY *of the* WORLD. H4ᵛ-S2. *The Judgment of* PARIS. S5ᵛ-T1ᵛ.

*SEMELE.* T5ᵛ-X8ᵛ. *vol. 3. Poems upon ſeveral Occaſions.* B1ᵛ-U8 *[Occaſions* (no period) L1ᵛ, N3ᵛ, P1, P3ᵛ, R3ᵛ]

CW] *vol. 1:* L6 THE [L6ᵛ blank] T8ᵛ Ld. *Touch.* 2I3 SCCNE [SCENE] *vol. 2:* C8ᵛ It G5 THE [G5ᵛ blank] L3 Eccho [*sic*] S3 THE [S3ᵛ blank] *vol. 3:* E1ᵛ Could [Cou'd] G3 SONG. [*SONG.*] I3 B [But] I8ᵛ 32 Ma- [32 Megalenſian] Q3ᵛ EPISTLE [OF] Q7 A[Q7ᵛ blank] R4ᵛ Fo [*For*] T8 Thu, [Thus,] [no CW on *vol. 1:* A8, R3ᵛ, *vol. 2:* T5, U4ᵛ, X7ᵛ, X8; *vol. 3:* a1ᵛ, B7, D8, F3, G5ᵛ, H1ᵛ, H5, I4, K5, K6ᵛ, L3, M5ᵛ, N3ᵛ, N6, O4ᵛ, R6, S1ᵛ, S5ᵛ, S6.]

*Signing and numbering:* $4 signed (*-vol. 1* a3.4; *vol. 2* ᵗA4; *vol. 3* a2, A4, F3, I4, L3). On $1 of each signed gathering (except *vol. 1* sig. a1, B1; *vol. 2* sig. T1; plus *vol. 2* A2) in signature-line next fold 'VOL. I.' and according to volume with rom. numbers. Following errors in pagination and signatures: *vol. 1:* 166 misnumbered as 176, 382 as 392, 383 as 783; *vol. 2:* 539 as 536, N4 missigned as M4; *vol. 3:* 930 misnumbered as 830, 1055 as 1505. No press figures.

*Type and ornaments:* text (vol. 1, B3): 31 ll., 144(155) x 80 mm., 93 R. The prologues to *LL, MB, WW* and the epilogues to *OB, DD, WW* are headed by a double row of type ornaments; Dryden's commendatory poem, the *DD* prologue, and the *LL* epilogue by a single row of type ornaments; the *MB* epilogue is headed by a triple row of type ornaments; Steele's commendatory poem is headed by a double rule. Each act opening has a double to quadruple row of type orn. Scenes are headed by a single or double row of type orn. Ornamental initials begin each act of each play, *Judgment of Paris,* and *Semele* (except Act II). Each poem begins with a 2-line capital and is headed by a rule if it does not begin the page. Scene VI, Act IV, *DD* is misnumbered 'VII.' Scene III, Act IV, *LL,* is misnumbered 'II.' and Scene IV, Act V, is misnumbered 'VIII.'

*Notes:* 'A Pindarique Ode, Humbly Offer'd to the Queen' and 'Homer's Hymn to Venus' have half-titles. Each play, the masque, and the opera have a head-title. The first collected edition of Congreve's works and the first in which the plays are divided into scenes. The Falkland prologue is attributed to its author for the first time. Rebound with original boards.

PR3360 .D10

## 107.  1717

[*General title in Vol. 1 only*] THE | WORKS | OF | Mr. *William Congreve;* | In THREE VOLUMES. | Containing his | PLAYS *and* POEMS. || || *LONDON,* | Printed for *J. Tonſon:* And Sold by *W. Taylor* in *Pater-* | *Noſter-Row,* and *W. Meares* and *J. Browne* without | *Temple-Bar.* MDCCXVII.

[*vol. titles*] as in 1710 (106.)

*Collation:* 8°. *vol. 1:* π1 A⁸ a⁴ B-2H⁸2I⁶χ1; *vol. 2:* ᵗA⁴ A-X⁸; *vol. 3:* A⁴ a² B-U⁸.

*Contents:* as in 1710 except for *vol. 1:* π1 general title (verso blank); *vol. 3:* A1 vol. title (verso blank); A2 section-title (verso blank); A3 contents; A4ᵛ errata; a1 epistle to Halifax.

*Notes:* Another issue. The signature suggests that the Halifax epistle in vol. 3 of the 1717 issue has been bound in the position originally intended. In original leather binding. Gilt title on binding of Vol. 2 and 3 reads 'CONGRE: | WORKS | Vol. II. [III]'; on vol. 1 'CONGREVE'S | WORKS | VOL. I.'

PR3360 .D17

## 108. 1719

[*General title in vol. 1 only.*] THE | WORKS | OF | Mr. *William Congreve:* | In TWO VOLUMES. | Conſiſting of HIS | PLAYS and POEMS. || The THIRD EDITION, Revis'd by | the AUTHOR. || *LONDON:* | Printed for JACOB TONSON, at *Shakeſpear's* | *Head* over-againſt *Katharine-Street* in | the *Strand.* M DCC XIX.

[*vol. titles*] *vol. 1:* THE | WORKS | OF | Mr. *William Congreve.* | VOLUME *the* FIRST. | CONTAINING | [three lines braced to the right] *The* OLD BATCHELOR. | *The* DOUBLE DEALER. | LOVE *for* LOVE. [to the right] Comedies. || [orn. T24] || [imprint and date as in general title]
*vol. 2:* [as in vol. 1 except for vol. no., comma after 'CONTAINING,' and list of contents and with double rule instead of ornament.]

*Section-titles: vol. 1,* A6: THE | Old Batchelor. | A | COMEDY. || [4-line motto from Horace and 1-line ack.] || [orn. T13] || Printed in the YEAR 1719. F9: THE | Double-Dealer. | A | COMEDY. || [1-line motto from Horace and 1-line ack.; 4-line motto from Terence and ack.] || orn. T94] || Printed in the YEAR M DCC XX. M3: *LOVE* for *LOVE.* | A | COMEDY. || [2-line motto from Horace and ack.] || [orn. T26] || Printed in the YEAR M DCC XX. *vol. 2,* A2: THE | *MOURNING BRIDE.* | A | TRAGEDY. || [2-line motto from Ovid and 1-line ack.] || [orn. T13] || Printed in the YEAR M DCC XIX. E1: THE | WAY *of the* WORLD. | A | COMEDY. || [3-line motto from Horace and ack.] || [orn. T26] || Printed in the YEAR M DCC XX. K9: THE

| JUDGMENT | OF | *PARIS:* | A | MASQUE. ‖ [1-line motto from Ovid and 1-line ack.] ‖ Printed in the YEAR M DCC XX. L2: *SEMELE.* | AN | OPERA. ‖ [3-line motto from Seneca and 1-line ack.] ‖ [orn. T13] ‖ Printed in the YEAR M DCC XX. M8: POEMS | UPON | *Several Occaſions.* ‖ 2-line motto from Horace and ack.] ‖ [orn. T27] ‖ Printed in the YEAR M DCC XX. S10: A | PINDARIQUE | ODE, | Humbly Offer'd to the | QUEEN, | On the Victorious Progreſs of | Her MAJESTY's Arms, under the Conduct | of the Duke of MARLBOROUGH. ‖ To which is prefix'd, | A DISCOURSE on the PINDARIQUE ODE. ‖ [2-line motto from Horace and ack.] ‖ Printed in the YEAR M DCC XX. U2: *HOMER's* | HYMN | TO | *VENUS:* | Tranſlated into | *ENGLISH* VERSE. ‖ [orn. T24] ‖ Printed in the YEAR M DCC XX.

*Collation:* 12°. *vol. 1:* π1 A-R¹²S⁶χ1, 212 leaves, pp. [28] *3* 4–110 *111–127* 128–242 *243–255* 256–396 [= 394] [2]; *vol. 2:* π² A-U¹², 242 leaves, pp. [4] *1–13* 14–94 *95–107* 108–230 *231–235* 236–241 *242–249* 250–277 *278–285* 286–426 *427–428* 429–458 *459–460* 461–478 *479–480.*

*Contents: vol. 1:* π1ʳ⁻ᵛ blank; A1 general title (verso blank); A2 vol. title (verso blank); A3 preface to the edition (fact⁴) headed by orn. (T28); on A5 orn. (T29); A5ᵛ blank; A6 *OB* s-t (verso blank); A7 dedicatory epistle (orn. initial⁴) headed by orn. (T30); A9ᵛ Southerne's commendatory poem; on A10 Marsh's commendatory poem; A11 Higgons' commendatory poem; A11ᵛ Falkland's prologue; on A12 orn. (T31); A12ᵛ prologue; on B1 orn. (T32); B1ᵛ dramatis personae (with cast); B2 *OB* text (orn. initial⁶) headed by orn. (T33) and HT; F8 epilogue; on F8ᵛ orn. (T29); F9 *DD* s-t (verso blank); F10 dedicatory epistle (orn. initial⁶) headed by orn. (T34); G1 Dryden's commendatory poem; on G2 orn. (T27); G2ᵛ prologue; on G3 orn. (T35); G3ᵛ dramatis personae (with cast); G4 *DD* text (orn. initial⁶) headed by orn. (T36) and HT; on M1ᵛ orn. (T14); M2 epilogue; on M2ᵛ orn. (T27); M3 *LL* s-t (verso blank); M4 dedicatory epistle (orn. initial⁶) headed by orn. (T36); M5ᵛ prologue; M6ᵛ epilogue; M7ᵛ dramatis personae (with cast); M8 *LL* text (orn. initial⁶) headed by orn. (T37) and HT; χ1ʳ⁻ᵛ blank.

*vol. 2:* π1–2ʳ⁻ᵛ blank; A1 vol. title (verso blank); A2 *MB* s-t (verso blank); A3 Steele's commendatory poem; A4 dedicatory epistle (fact⁶) headed by orn. (T28); A5ᵛ prologue; A6ᵛ dramatis personae (with cast); A7 *MB* text (orn. initial⁶) headed by orn. (T30) and HT; D12 epilogue; on D12ᵛ orn. (T32); E1 *WW* s-t (verso blank); E2 dedicatory epistle (fact⁶) headed by orn. (T36); E4ᵛ prologue; E5ᵛ dramatis personae (with cast); E6 *WW* text (orn. initial⁶) headed by orn. (T33) and HT; K8 epilogue; on K8ᵛ orn. (T38); K9 *JP* s-t (verso blank); K10 *JP* text (orn. initial⁶) headed by orn. (T39) and HT; on L1 orn. (T40); L1ᵛ blank; L2 *Semele* s-t (verso blank); L3 argument (orn. initial⁵) headed by orn. (T37); on L4 orn. (T35); L4ᵛ dramatis personae; L5

*Semele* text (orn. initial[4]) headed by orn. (T34) and HT; M7ᵛ blank; M8 *Poems* s-t (verso blank); M9 dedicatory epistle (orn. initial[5]) headed by orn. (T39, inverted); on M10 orn. (T26); M10ᵛ blank; M11 text of the poems (orn. initial[5]) headed by orn. (T30); S10 queen's pindarique ode s-t (verso blank); U2, *Homer's Hymn* s-t (verso blank); on U11ᵛ orn. (T35); U12 table of the poems; χ1ʳ⁻ᵛ blank.

RT] *vol. 1. The* OLD BATCHELOR. B3-F7ᵛ; *The* DOUBLE-DEALER· G4ᵛ-M1ᵛ [DOUBLE-DEALER (no period) G12ᵛ, H12ᵛ, I12ᵛ]; LOVE *for* LOVE. M8ᵛ-S6ᵛ. *vol. 2. The* MOURNING BRIDE. A7ᵛ-D11ᵛ; *The* WAY *of the* WORLD. E6ᵛ-K7ᵛ [WORLD: E6ᵛ; WORLR. F9, G9, H9, I9]; *The Judgment of* PARIS. K10ᵛ-L1; *SEMELE.* L5ᵛ-M7; *Poems upon Jeveral Occaſions.* M11ᵛ-U11ᵛ [*Occaſions* (no period) N2ᵛ, O5, P12ᵛ, Q6, S8ᵛ, S11, T10ᵛ, U1]

CW] *vol. 1:* A5 THE [A5ᵛ blank] A8ᵛ *the [they]* G5ᵛ *(Cyn-)thia, [thia;]* I6ᵛ SCENE. [SCENE] N5ᵛ *VAEN-[VALENTINE.]* O1 pardon. [Pardon.] *vol. 2:* A6ᵛ THE F12ᵛ and H10ᵛ that [That] L1 *SEME-* [L1ᵛ blank] L10 SCENE. [SCENE] M7 POEMS [M7ᵛ blank] M10 THE [M10ᵛ blank] P3 And [What] R4 Still [Sill] [no cw on *vol. 1:* K9ᵛ, O2ᵛ, P5ᵛ, Q7ᵛ, R5ᵛ; *vol. 2.* C6ᵛ, D1, H7ᵛ, P9, U10]

*Signing and numbering:* $5 signed (-*vol. 1* S4.5; *vol. 2* E4); On $1 of each gathering (except *vol. 1* sig. B1; plus *vol. 2,* sig. E2) in signature-line next fold 'VOL. I.' and according to volume with rom. numbers. Following errors in pagination and signatures: *vol. 1:* 110 misnumbered as 112, 238 as 239, 239 as 238, 301 as 201, 310 as 311, 311 as 310, 323 as 332; *vol. 2:* 253 as 453, 421 as 41, F4 missigned as E4. No press figures.

*Type and ornaments:* text (vol. 1, C3): 38 ll., 120(131) x 72 mm., 63 R. Commendatory poems, prologues, epilogues, and each act of the plays and opera are headed by a small cast orn.; scenes are separated usually by small cast orn. Each act, except the first, of the plays begins with a factotum; the acts of *Semele* begin with a 4-line orn. initial. Poems are usually headed by a rule except when they begin the page. Each commendatory poem, prologue, and epilogue begins with a 2-line cap.

*Notes:* The first edition in which the speaker's name is centered on the page. Scene VIII, Act IV, *MB,* misnumbered as 'VII.' Scene VII, Act III, *WW* misnumbered as 'VI.' Bound in brown leather. Has book plate of Richard Boycott.

PR3360 .D19

## 109.

Fine-paper copy of the 1719 *Works*.

*Notes:* The pagination error on p. 421, Vol. 2, has been corrected; the variants in RT on vol. 2, E6ᵛ, S8ᵛ have been corrected. Leaves R4.5, vol. 2, are apparently cancels, although the textual changes are slight. Vol. 2 has 1 prefixed and 1 concluding unsigned leaf. Bearing the book plate of the Duke of Leeds, this copy was Lot 156 in Sotheby's catalog of the Leeds Library (1930) and probably Congreve's own copy (See *Congreve*, 98; and p. 7). Purchased from Percy Dobell & Son, 1959. Bound in red morocco.

PR3360 .D19a

## 110. 1725

[*General title*] as in 1719 (108.) except for | In THREE VOLUMES. | [2 lines] ‖ The FOURTH EDITION. ‖ [2 lines] | Head, ... | ... M DCC XXV.

[*vol. titles*] *vol. 1:* as in 1719 (108.) except for omission of *Love for Love* in contents lines and ‖ *London:* | Printed for JACOB TONSON, in the | *Strand.* M DCC XXV.

*vol. 2–3:* as in vol. 1 except for vol. number and contents list; vol. 2–3 have '*Congreve:*' and vol. 3 has 'CONTAINING,'; vol. 2 has a different orn. (T41) and vol. 3 has double rule in place of orn.

*Section-titles:* as in 1719 ed. (108.) except for imprint date and the following: imprint dates for *DD, LL, MB, WW* are in arabic; orn. on *DD* and *Poems* is T41; orn. on *WW* is T42; no s-t for *Homer's Hymn*.

*Collation:* 12°. *vol. 1:* π1 A-M¹² N⁶χ1; 152 leaves, pp. [28] *3* 4–125 *126–147* 148–272 *273–4* [=272] [4]; *vol. 2:* π1 A-M¹²χ1, 146 leaves, pp. [2] *1–13* 14–174 *175–187* 188–283 *284–286* [4]; *vol. 3:* π1 A-Q¹²χ1, 194 leaves, pp. [2] *1–15* 16–147 *148–153* 154–159 *160–167* 168–197 *198–205* 206–336 *337–338* 339–365 *366* 367–382 *383–384* [2].

*Contents: vol. 1:* π1ʳ⁻ᵛ blank; A1 general title (verso blank); A2 vol. title (verso blank); A3 preface (orn. initial⁴) headed by orn. (T43); on A5 orn. (T44); A5ᵛ blank; A6 *OB* s-t (verso blank); A7 dedicatory epistle (orn. initial⁴) headed by orn. (T45); A9ᵛ Southerne's commendatory poem; on A10 Marsh's commendatory poem; A11 Higgons' commendatory poem; A11ᵛ Falkland's prologue; on A12 orn. (T41); A12$^v$ prologue; on B1 orn. (T32); B1$^v$ dramatis personae (with cast); B2 *OB* text (orn. initial[5]) headed by orn. (T46) and HT; on G3 orn. (T13); G3$^v$ epilogue; on G4 orn. (T32); G4$^v$ blank; G5 *DD* s-t (verso blank); G6 dedicatory epistle (orn. initial[4]) headed by orn. (T47); G10$^v$ Dryden's commendatory poem; G12$^v$ prologue; on H1 orn. (T44); H1$^v$ dramatis personae (with cast); H2 *DD* text (orn. initial[5]) headed by orn. (T2) and HT; on N4$^v$ orn. (T58); N5 epilogue; on N5$^v$ orn. (T75); N6$^{r-v}$ blank; $\chi$1$^{r-v}$ blank. *vol. 2:* $\pi$1$^{r-v}$ blank; A1 vol. title (verso blank); A2 *LL* s-t (verso blank); A3 dedicatory epistle (orn. initial[4]) headed by orn. (T47); A5$^v$ prologue; A6$^v$ dramatis personae (with cast); A7 *LL* text (orn. initial[6]) headed by orn. (T43) and HT; on H3$^v$ orn. (T41); H4 epilogue; on H4$^v$ orn. (T87); H5 *MB* s-t (verso blank); H6 dedicatory epistle (fact[4]) headed by orn. (T45); H8$^v$ prologue; on H9 orn. (T76); H9$^v$ dramatis personae (with cast); H10 *MB* text (orn. initial[6]) headed by orn. (T48) and HT; M10$^v$ epilogue; on M11 orn. (T13); M11$^v$ blank; M12$^{r-v}$ blank; $\chi$1$^{r-v}$ blank. *vol. 3:* $\pi$1$^{r-v}$ blank; A1 vol. title (verso blank); A2 *WW* s-t (verso blank); A3 dedicatory epistle (fact[6]) headed by orn. (T43); A5$^v$ Steele's commendatory verses; A6$^v$ prologue; A7$^v$ dramatis personae (with cast); A8 *WW* text (orn. initial[6]) headed by orn. (T47) and HT; G2$^v$ epilogue; on G3 orn. (T49); G3$^v$ blank; G4 *Judgment* s-t (verso blank); G5 *Judgment* text (orn. initial[6]) headed by orn. (T50) and HT; G8$^v$ blank; G9 *Semele* s-t (verso blank); G10 argument (fact[5]) headed by orn. (T2); on G11 orn. (T29); G11$^v$ dramatis personae; G12 *Semele* text (orn. initial[4]) headed by orn. (T43) and HT; on I3 orn. (T42); I3$^v$ blank; I4 *Poems* s-t (verso blank); I5 dedicatory epistle (orn. initial[5]) headed by orn. (T48); I6$^v$ blank; I7 *Poems* text (orn. initial[5]) headed by orn. (T28); on O12$^v$ orn. (T32); P1 queen's pindarique ode s-t (verso blank); on P5$^v$ orn. (T51); on Q11$^v$ orn. (T32); Q12 table of the poems; $\chi$1$^{r-v}$ blank.

RT] *vol. 1: The* OLD BATCHELOR. B2$^v$-G3; *The* DOUBLE-DEALER. H2$^v$-N4$^v$; *vol. 2:* LOVE *for* LOVE. A7$^v$-H3$^v$ [LOVE (no period) C3]; *The* MOURNING BRIDE. H10$^v$-M10 [BRIDB. H10$^v$, I10$^v$, K8$^v$, L8$^v$, M8$^v$]; *vol. 3: The* WAY *of the* WORLD. A8$^v$-G2; *The Judgment of* PARIS. G5$^v$-G8; *SEMELE.* G12$^v$-I3; *Poems upon ſeveral Occaſions.* I7$^v$-Q11$^v$ [*Occaſirns.* L4$^v$].

CW] *vol. 1:* A5 THE [A5$^v$ blank] A7$^v$ (Acknow-)ledgment [ledgement] G1$^v$ *BUFFE.* [*BLUFFE.*] G9 ther [there] M12$^v$ *MASK-*[*MASKWELL*] N2 Lord [Lady] *vol. 2:* A12$^v$ *TRAP-*[*TRAPLAND.*] E12$^v$ Face: *vol. 3:* C12$^v$ remove E11$^v$ *tha* [that] G3 THE [G3$^v$ blank] G8 *SEME-* [G8$^v$ blank] I3 POEMS [I3$^v$ blank] I6 THE [I6$^v$ blank] P12$^v$ What [no cw on *vol. 3*, Q6]

*Signing and numbering:* $5 (-*vol. 1* N4.5; *vol. 3* Q4; + *vol. 1* G6; *vol. 2* H6) on $1 of each signed gathering (except *vol. 1*, sig. B1, H1; *vol. 3*, H1, Q1) in signature line next fold 'VOL. I.' and according to vol. with rom. numbers. Press figures are present as follows: *vol. 1:* A8$^v$-4, C2$^v$-4, D2$^v$-5, E11$^v$-4, F8$^v$-5, G6$^v$-5, H12$^v$-4, I11$^v$-4, K7$^v$-4; *vol. 2:* A11-7, B2$^v$-5, D11-7, E12$^v$-7, M7-5; *vol. 3:* A12-7, B5$^v$-5, C11$^v$-6, E2$^v$-3, F1$^v$-5, G12-4, H8$^v$-7, I1$^v$-4, K7$^v$-4, L5-6,

N8-4, N11-4, O7$^v$-4, P12-3, Q12-8. Following errors in pagination and signatures: *vol. 1:* 51 misnumbered as 57; *vol. 3:* 62 as 92, 95 as 65. *vol. 2:* I2 missigned as H2.

*Type and ornaments:* text (*vol. 1*, B3), 35 ll., 120(129) x 72 mm., 69 R. Commendatory poems, prologues, epilogues, and each act of the plays and opera are headed by a small cast ornament; scenes are usually headed by a small cast orn.; poems are usually headed by a rule except when they begin the page. Each act begins with an ornamental initial (4-6 ll.) or factotum (4-6 ll.) Commendatory poems, prologues, and epilogues begin with a 2-line capital.

*Notes:* In original leather binding. The following errors in numbering scenes: Scene XVI, Act IV, *DD*, misnumbered as 'XV.'; Scene IX, Act IV, *LL*, as 'VI.'; Scene VII, Act III, *WW*, misnumbered 'VI.'

PR3360 .D25

## 111. 1730

[*General title*] as in 1725 (110.) except for ‖ The FIFTH EDITION. ‖ *LONDON:* | Printed for J. TONSON in the *Strand.* | [partial rule] | M DCC XXX.

[*vol. titles*] *vol. 1:* as in 1725 (110.) except for ‖ [orn. T25] ‖ *LONDON:* | Printed for J. TONSON in the *Strand.* | [partial rule] | M DCC XXX. *vol. 2–3:* as in vol. 1 except for vol. no. and contents list; vol. 2–3 have '*Congreve:*'; vol. 2 has different orn. (T52) and vol. 3 has double rule in place of orn.

*Section-titles:* as in 1725 (110.) except for imprint date and ornaments on the following section-titles—*DD*, T53; *LL*, T9; *MB*, T54; *WW*, T55; *Semele*, T10; *Poems*, T42—italicized colon after '*PARIS*', and the following imprint on *Semele:* 'Printed in the YEAR 1730.'

*Collation:* 12°. *vol. 1:* π1 A-M$^{12}$ N$^6$χ$^1$, 152 leaves, pp. [28] *3* 4–125 *126–147* 148–272 *273–274* [=272] [4]; *vol. 2:* π1 A-M$^{12}$ χ$^1$, 146 leaves, pp. [2] *1–13* 14–174 *175–187* 188–283 *284–286* [4]; *vol. 3:* π1 A-Q$^{12}$ χ$^1$, 194 leaves, pp. [2] *1–15* 16–147 *148–153* 154–159 *160–167* 168–197 *198–205* 206–336 *337–338* 339–365 *366* 367–382 *383–384* [2].

*Contents:* as in 1725 (110.) except for different ornamental initials and factotums, and ornaments as follows: *vol. 1:* A7 T48; A12 T55; B1 T38 (Plomer 103); G3 T49; G4 T56; G6 T46; H1 T58; N4$^v$ T26; N5$^v$ T57. *vol. 2:* A3 T46; H3$^v$ T55; H4$^v$ fleuron; H6 T48; H9 T42; H10 T2. *vol. 3:* A3 T46; A8 T48; G3 T59; G5 T2; G10 T45; G12 T46; I3 T26; I5 T43; I7 T48; O12$^v$ T56; P5$^v$ T59; Q11$^v$ T31.

RT] as in 1725 (110.) except for the following variants instead of those in 110.: *'Occaſions'* [no period] *vol. 3*, K9, M10, P9; and *'Occaſioas.'* *vol. 3*, K11, M12, P11.

CW] *vol 1:* A5 THE [A5ᵛ blank] G1ᵛ *BLUFFE.* M12ᵛ *MASK-* [*MASKWELL,*] *vol. 2:* A12ᵛ *TRAP-[TRAPLAND.*] E12ᵛ Face: G12 (ſe-)ious [rious] *vol. 3:* C12ᵛ remove E1 Mr [Mrs.] E4 (Fro-)lick [ck] E11ᵛ *that* G3 THE [G3ᵛ blank] G8 *SEME-* [G8ᵛ blank] I3 POEMS [I3ᵛ blank] I6 THE [I6ᵛ blank] O3 A [As] P12ᵛ What [no cw on *vol. 3*, N6ᵛ].

*Signing and numbering:* $5 (-*vol. 1* N4.5; + *vol. 1*, G6, *vol. 2*, H6). On $1 of each signed gathering in signature line next fold 'VOL. I.' and according to vol. with rom. numbers. Press figures are present as follows: *vol. 1:* B12-6, E8-4, G8-7, K8-7; *vol. 2:* B1ᵛ-4, C5ᵛ-4, D11-4, D11ᵛ-7, E12ᵛ-4, F12-7, G2ᵛ-7, G12-4, H12ᵛ-4, I1ᵛ-3, K5ᵛ-4, K12ᵛ-4, L11ᵛ-4, M2ᵛ-7, M8-4; *vol. 3:* A11ᵛ-7, A12ᵛ-4, B2ᵛ-7, C6ᵛ-7, D6ᵛ-7, E8-7, F1ᵛ-7, G2ᵛ-7, H6ᵛ-4, I8ᵛ-7, M12ᵛ-4, O6-4, O11-7, P6ᵛ-4. Following errors in pagination: *vol. 3:* 237 misnumbered as 337, 320 as 20.

*Type:* text (*vol. 1*, B3), 35 ll., 122(131) x 73 mm., 69 R.

*Notes:* Apparently a paginal resetting of the 1725 edition, this edition differs primarily in the ornaments. It repeats the scene misnumberings of the 1725 edition. The volume title of each volume bears the signature of Jean-Sylvain Bailly, first mayor of Paris.

PR3360 .D30

## 112. 1730

*No general title and no vol. titles*]

*Section-titles:* as in vol. 3, 1730 (111.) except for omission of *WW*.

*Notes:* A binding of G4-G12 H-Q¹² of vol. 3, 1730 (111.) in the following order: I4-I12 G4-G12 H12 I3 K-Q¹². On $1 of each signed gathering in signature line next fold 'VOL. III.' The '3' on p. 320 has printed in this copy.

PR3360 .D30a

## 113. 1736

[*vol. titles*] *vol. 1:* THE | WORKS | OF | Mr. *William Congreve.* | Volume *the* FIRST. | CONTAINING | [on the left braced to the right] *The* OLD BATCHELLOR. | *The* DOUBLE DEALER. [on the right braced to the left] LOVE *for* LOVE. | And *The* | MOURNING BRIDE. || [orn. (18 x 30): floral basket] || *DUBLIN:* Printed, by THEO. JONES, | For GEORGE RISK, at *Shakeſpear's* Head, GEORGE | EWING, at the Angel and Bible, and WILLIAM | SMITH, at the *Hercules*, in *Dame-ſtreet*, Bookſellers, | M,DCC,XXXVI. *vol. 2:* [as in *vol. 1* except for contents and orn. (17 x 33): beast with crossed clubs]

*Section-titles: vol. 1:* A1: THE | Old Batchelor. | A | COMEDY. || [4-line motto from Horace and 1-line ack.] || Written by Mr. CONGREVE. || [orn. (9 x 27): twisted floral urn with single flower on sides] ||| *DUBLIN:* | Printed for G. and A. EWING, W. SMITH, Sen. | J. EXSHAW, and H. BRADLEY, Bookſellers in | *Dame-ſtreet*, 1760. ²A1: THE | Double-Dealer. | A | COMEDY. || [1-line motto from Horace and 1-line ack.; 3-line motto from Terence and 1-line ack.] || [orn. (24 x 31): flowers in vase] || [except for the omission of *'DUBLIN:'* and a different imprint date ('MDCC,XXXV') identical with imprint of vol. title]. ³A1: *LOVE* for *LOVE.* | A | COMEDY. || [2-line motto from Horace and 1-line ack.] || [orn. as on vol. t-p.] || *DUBLIN:* | Printed for GEORGE RISK, at *Shakeſpear's* Head, GEORGE | and ALEXANDER EWING, at the *Angel* and *Bible,* | and WILLIAM SMITH, at the *Hercules*, in *Dame-* | *ſtreet*, Bookſellers. MDCCXLVIII. ⁴A1: THE | MOURNING BRIDE. | A | TRAGEDY. || [2-line motto from Ovid and 1-line ack.] || [orn. as on vol. t-p] || DUBLIN: | Printed for G. RISK at *Shakeſpear's Head*, G. and | A. EWING at the *Angel* and *Bible*, and W. SMITH at | the *Hercules* in *Dames-ſtreet*, [sic] Bookſellers. M,DCC,LIII. *vol. 2:* A1: THE | WAY *of the* WORLD. | A | COMEDY. || Written by | Mr. WILLIAM CONGREVE. || [3-line motto from Horace and ack.] || [orn. (19 x 20): female bust in scrollwork] ||| DUBLIN: | Printed for G. and A. EWING, W. SMITH, J. EXSHAW, | and H. BRADLEY, Bookſellers, in *Dame-ſtreet.* | [partial rule] | M DCC LIX. E1: THE | JUDGMENT | OF | *PARIS;* | A | MASQUE || [1-line motto from Ovid and 1-line ack.] || Printed in the YEAR MDCCXXXV. E6: *SEMELE.* | AN | OPERA. || [3-line motto from Seneca and 1-line ack.] || [orn. (22 x 28): standing lion on ornamented base] || Printed in the YEAR MDCCXXXV. F12: POEMS | UPON | *Several Occaſions.* || [2-line motto from Hor. and ack.] || [orn. as on vol. 1 t-p] || Printed in the Year MDCCXXXV. M10: A | PINDARIQUE | ODE, | Humbly Offer'd to the | QUEEN, | On the Victorious Progreſs of | Her MAJESTY's Arms, under the Conduct | of the Duke of MARLBOROUGH. || To which is prefix'd, | A DISCOURSE on the PINDARIQUE ODE. || [2-line motto from Horace and ack.] || Printed in the YEAR MDCCXXXV.

*Collation: vol. 1:* 12°. ᵗA⁴ A-F⁶ˣA⁶ 2A-2C¹² 2D⁶ 3A⁶ 3B-3E¹² (3E6.7 lacking)
4A-4C¹²χ¹, 177 leaves, pp. [8] *1–3* 4–71 *72;* ²*1–15* 16–95 *96;* ³*1–8* 9–94
99–106 *107–108* [=104]; 4*1–9* 10–70 *71–72* [2]; *vol. 2:* π³A-N¹² O⁹, 168
leaves, pp. [6] *1–13* 14–94 *95–99* 100–105 *106–113* 114–143 *144–151*
152–282 *283–284* 285–328 [2].

*Contents: vol. 1:* ᵗA1 vol. title (verso blank); ᵗA2 preface (fact⁵) headed by
orn. ([22 x 68] female face framed in oval, with cornucopias, within border);
on ᵗA4 orn. ([32 x 50] three flowers with foliage); ᵗA4ᵛ blank; A1 *OB* s-t; A1ᵛ
dramatis personae; A2 *OB* text (cap²) headed by orn. ([22 x 68] jester's cap
above floral urn, foliage, without border) and HT; F6ᵛ blank; ˣA1 *DD* s-t (verso
blank); ˣA2 dedicatory epistle (fact⁵) headed by triple row type orn.;
ˣA5ᵛ Dryden's commendatory poem; on ˣA6ᵛ orn. ([29 x 31] headdress with
perched birds); ²A1 prologue; ²A1ᵛ dramatis personae; ²A2 *DD* text (fact⁷)
headed by orn. ([23 x 75] floral urn with cornucopias, within border) and HT;
²D6ᵛ epilogue; ³A1 *LL* s-t (verso blank); ³A2 dedicatory epistle (cap³) headed
by orn. ([25 x 75] female face in circular frame with vines and flowers, within
border); ³A3ᵛ prologue; ³A4ᵛ dramatis personae; ³A5 *LL* text (orn. initial⁸)
headed by orn. ([22 x 71] winged head above crossed trumpets with birds and
foliage, without border) and HT; 3E12 epilogue; on 3E12ᵛ orn. ([33 x 39] flowers
in vase); 4A1 *MB* s-t (verso blank); 4A2 dedicatory epistle headed by double
rule (cap²); 4A3ᵛ prologue; on 4A4 orn. [as on 3E12ᵛ]; 4A4ᵛ dramatis personae;
4A5 *MB* text (cap³) headed by orn. [as on ᵗA2] and HT; on 4C11ᵛ orn. ([38 x 41]
bust on pedestal with birds); 4C12 epilogue (verso blank); χ1ʳ⁻ᵛ blank. *vol. 2:*
π1ʳ⁻ᵛ blank; π2 vol. title (verso blank); π3 table of the poems; A1 *WW* s-t (verso
blank); A2 dedicatory epistle (cap³) headed by orn. ([20 x 71] floral urn with
winged figures holding scrollwork at sides, within border); A4ᵛ Steele's commendatory poem; A5ᵛ prologue; on A6 orn. ([17 x 20] floral); A6ᵛ dramatis
personae; A7 *WW* text (cap⁴) headed by orn. ([20 x 72] head with floral basket
above, wings below, interlaced scrollwork, no border) and HT; D12 epilogue;
on D12ᵛ orn. [as on vol. 2, A1]; E1 *Judgment* s-t (verso blank); E2 *Judgment*
text (fact⁶) headed by orn. ([25 x 72] figure with pipe on lyre-shaped pedestal,
with griffin-like figures, no border) and HT; E5ᵛ blank; E6 *Semele* s-t (verso
blank); E7 argument (fact⁶) headed by orn. ([23 x 75] foliage with springing
hare and deer, no border); on E8 orn. ([58 x 53] cherubs with instruments seated
against floral urn); E8ᵛ dramatis personae; E9 *Semele* text (fact⁷) headed by
orn. ([25 x 70] seated nude figures and floral urns, within border) and HT;
on F12 orn. ([43 x 42] Cupid seated on pedestal, with birds); F12ᵛ blank; G1
*Poems* s-t (verso blank); G2 dedicatory epistle (fact⁶) headed by orn. ([28 x 75]
beast's head with vines and birds, within border); on G3 orn. ([47 x 51] single
flower in urn on pedestal); G3ᵛ blank; G4 text of poems headed by orn. (as on
vol. 2, E7); on M9ᵛ orn. (as on vol. 2, E8); M10 queen's pindarique ode s-t
(verso blank); on O8ᵛ orn. ([34 x 50] drummer with sticks raised); O9ʳ⁻ᵛ blank.

RT] *vol. 1: The Old Batchelor.* A2ᵛ-F6; *The* DOUBLE-DEALER. ²A2ᵛ-²D6
[DEALBR. ²C1, ²D4ᵛ; DOUBLLE- ²C8ᵛ]; LOVE *for* LOVE. ³A5ᵛ-E11ᵛ; *The*

MOURNING BRIDE. ⁴A5ᵛ-⁴C11ᵛ [BIRDE. ⁴C10]. *vol. 2: The* WAY *of the* WORLD. A7ᵛ-D11ᵛ [WOLRD. C12]; *The Judgment of* PARIS. E2ᵛ-E5; *SEMELE.* E9ᵛ-F12 [*SEMELE* (no period) F2; *SEMELE.* F8ᵛ; *SEMELE.* F9]; POEMS *upon ſeveral Occaſions.* G4ᵛ-O8ᵛ [POMBS G5ᵛ; *Occaſions* (no period) G7, H5; *on* G11-G12ᵛ; POEES H8].

CW] *vol. 1:* πA4 THE [πA4ᵛ blank] A6ᵛ ACT. [ACT] E6ᵛ wilt ²A6ᵛ where [Where] ²B12ᵛ Care. [*Car.*] ⁴B12ᵛ Zara. *vol. 2:* A12ᵛ *Mira.* C6 *Fain.* [*Fain*] C7ᵛ *Mill.* [*Mil.*] C12ᵛ *Wil.* [*Mil.*] E2ᵛ In [*In*] E4ᵛ IV. Gentle [*Gentle*] E5 *SEMELE* [E5ᵛ blank] F6 JUNO. [JUNO,] F8ᵛ *JUNO.* [*JUNO*] F12 POEMS [F12ᵛ blank] G3 THE [G3ᵛ blank] L7ᵛ T [Thee] M5 An- [22 Andromeda,] N9 Tha [That] [no cw on vol. 1, ³E2ᵛ]

*Signing and numbering:* $5 (-*vol. 1:* πA3.4, A4.5, B4.5, C4.5, D2, D4.5, E4.5, F4.5 ˣA4.5, ²D4.5, ³A4.5, ⁴A3; *vol. 2,* A4, O5) signed. Following errors in pagination and signatures: *vol. 1:* p. ²82 misnumbered as 22, B3 missigned as F3, D1 as C1; *vol. 2:* p. 206 misnumbered as 306, 214 as 114, 215 as 115; G2 missigned as G, G4 as G2. *vol. 2,* π3 has 'VOL. II' in signature line next fold and is signed P. No press figures. The three prefatory leaves may be the remainder of O gathering.

*Type and ornaments:* text (*vol. 1,* A3): 42 ll., 139(147) x 73 mm., 66 R.; (*vol. 1,* ²A4): 40 ll., 132(141) x 72 mm., 66 R. Dryden's and Steele's commendatory poems, the prologues to *LL* and *WW*, and the epilogues to *LL*, *MB*, and *WW* are headed by an ornament; the prologue to *MB* is headed by a double rule; all commendatory poems, prologues, and epilogues begin with a 2-line capital.

*Notes:* As the imprint dates and the separate pagination and signatures in the first volume indicate, the edition is a confused one, made up of plays designed for separate publication. See 84., 39. All the plays except *The Old Bachelor* follow the scene divisions of the Tonson editions of the *Works*. Only *The Old Bachelor* is printed without dedicatory epistle, prologue, or epilogue. Scene XVII, Act IV, *DD*, is misnumbered 'XVIII.', with the error continuing through the act.

PR3360 .D36

## 114. 1752

[*General title in vol. 1 only:*] THE | WORKS | OF | Mr. *William Congreve.* | IN THREE VOLUMES. | CONSISTING OF HIS | PLAYS and POEMS. ‖ *The Fifth Editton.* [*sic*] ‖ *LONDON:* | Printed for TONSON, in the *Strand.* | [partial rule] | M DCC LII.

[*vol. titles*] *vol. 1:* THE | WORKS | OF | Mr. *William Congreve.* | VOLUME *the* FIRST. | CONTAINING | [3 lines braced to the right]

*The* OLD BATCHELOR. | *The* DOUBLE DEALER. [to the right] Comedies. | *The* WAY *of the* WORLD. || [orn.: stylized flower (13 x 34)] || *LONDON:* | Printed for TONSON in the *Strand.* | [partial rule] | M DCC LII. *vol. 2–3:* [as in vol. 1 except for volume number and contents in two or three lines, a triangle of fleurons replacing the ornament; the imprint follows the general title; 'JUDGMENT' is spelled 'JUGEMENT' on vol. 2]

*Section-titles: vol. 1,* A1: THE OLD | BATCHELOUR, | A | COMEDY. | Written by Mr. *CONGREVE.* || [4-line motto from Horace and 1-line ack.] | [orn.: entwined scrollwork and vines (38 x 41)] | LONDON, | Printed for T. JOHNSON. || M. DCC. XX. ²A1: THE | DOUBLE- | DEALER. | A | COMEDY. | *Written by* Mr. CONGREVE. | [orn. as on *OB* section-title] | LONDON. | Printed for the Company of Bookſellers. ³A1: THE WAY | OF THE | WORLD | A | COMEDY. | *Writen* [*sic*] *by* Mr. CONGREVE. || [3-line motto from Horace and ack.] | [orn. as on *OB* section-title] | LONDON | Printed for the Company of Bookſellers. *vol. 2:* A1: LOVE FOR LOVE: | A | COMEDY. | *Writen* [*sic*] by Mr CONGREVE. || [2-line motto from Horace and ack.] | [orn.: flowers in vase (35 x 42)] | LONDON, | Printed for H: SCHEURLEER F-Z. || 1752. ²A1: THE | *MOURNING BRIDE.* | A | TRAGEDY. || [2-line motto from Ovid and 1-line ack.] || [orn.: pedestal scrollwork (24 x 43)] | LONDON, | Printed for H: SCHEURLEER, F-Z. || 1752. *vol. 3,* A1: *SEMELE.* | AN | OPERA. || [3-line motto from Seneca and 1-line ack.] || [orn.: head above wings (24 x 54)] || Printed in the YEAR 1752. C4: POEMS | UPON | *Several Occaſions.* | BY CONGREEVE [*sic*]. || [2-line motto from Horace and ack.] || [orn. as on *MB* section-title] || Printed in the YEAR MDCCLIII. M1: A | PINDARIQUE | ODE, | Humbly Offer'd to the | QUEEN, | On the Victorious Progreſs of | Her MAJESTY's Arms, under the Conduct | of the Duke of MARLBOROUGH. || To which is prefix'd, | A DISCOURSE on the PINDARIQUE ODE. || [2-line motto from Horace and ack.] || Printed in the YEAR MDCCXXX.

*Collation:* 8°. *vol. 1:* ᵖA⁵ A-F⁸ ²A-²G⁸ ³A-³G⁸ ³H³, 168 leaves, pp. [10] *1–13* 14–93 *94–96,* ²*1–3* 4–8 *9–11* 12 *13* 14–111 *112,* ³*1–3* 4–7 *8* 9 *10–11* 12–113 *114–118; vol. 2:* π1 A-H⁸ ²A-²F⁸ ²G⁶, 119 leaves, pp. [2] *1–12* 13–125 *126* [2], ²*1–11* 12–98 *99–101* 102–107 *108; vol. 3:* π1 A-O⁸, 113 leaves, pp. [2] *1–7* 8–37 *38–45* 46–176 *177–178* 179–205 *206* 207–222 *223–224.*

*Contents: vol. 1:* ᵖA1 general title (verso blank); ᵖA2 volume title (verso blank); ᵖA3 preface (orn. initial⁵) headed by orn. [rectangle of type orn. enclosing

5 rows of type orn.]; on <sup>π</sup>A5 orn. [three-stemmed leaf in urn within elaborate frame (38 x 55)]; <sup>π</sup>A5<sup>v</sup> blank; A1 *OB* section-title (verso blank); A2 dedicatory epistle (cap²) headed by double row of type orn.; A3<sup>v</sup> Southerne's commendatory poem headed by double row of type orn.; A4<sup>v</sup> Marsh's commendatory poem; A5 Higgons' commendatory poem; A5<sup>v</sup> Falkland's prologue; A6 prologue: A6<sup>v</sup> dramatis personae; A7 *OB* text (cap⁴) headed by double row of type orn. and HT; F7<sup>v</sup> epilogue; F8 Johnson book advertisement; ²A1 *DD* section-title; 2A1<sup>v</sup> *DD* mottoes; ²A2 dedicatory epistle headed by double row of type orn.; ²A5 Dryden's commendatory poem; ²A6 prologue; ²A6<sup>v</sup> dramatis personae; ²A7 *DD* text (cap⁴) headed by double row of type orn. and HT; ²G8<sup>v</sup> epilogue; ³A1 *WW* section-title (verso blank); ³A2 dedicatory epistle headed by triple row of type orn.; ³A4<sup>v</sup> prologue headed by double row of type orn.; ³A5<sup>v</sup> dramatis personae; ³A6 *WW* text (cap²) headed by double row of type orn. and HT; ³H1<sup>v</sup> epilogue headed by double row of type orn.; ³H2<sup>v</sup> Steele's commendatory poem headed by double row of type orn.; ³H3<sup>v</sup> Johnson book advertisement. *vol. 2:* π1 volume title (verso blank); A1 *LL* section-title (verso blank); A2 dedicatory epistle (cap²) headed by orn. [rect. of type orn. enclosing 2 rows of type orn.]; A3<sup>v</sup> anonymous prologue headed by row of type orn.; A4<sup>v</sup> prologue headed by double row of type orn.; A5<sup>v</sup> epilogue headed by row of type orn.; A6<sup>v</sup> dramatis personae; A7 *LL* text (cap³) headed by double row of type orn. and HT; H7<sup>v</sup> blank; H8<sup>r-v</sup> blank; ²A1 *MB* section-title (verso blank); ²A2 dedicatory epistle (fact⁴) headed by orn. [rect. of type orn. enclosing double row of type orn.]; ²A4<sup>v</sup> prologue headed by row of type orn.; ²A5<sup>v</sup> dramatis personae (with cast); ²A6 *MB* text (fact⁶) headed by orn. [rect. of type orn. enclosing 3 rows of type orn.] and HT; ²G2 epilogue; ²G3 *Judgment* text (fact⁶) headed by quadruple row of type orn.; ²G6<sup>v</sup> blank. *vol. 3:* π1 volume title (verso blank); A1 *Semele* section-title (verso blank); A2 *Semele* argument (fact⁵) headed by septuple row of type orn.; on A3 orn. [bird on pedestal (40 x 52)]; A3<sup>v</sup> dramatis personae; A4 *Semele* text (fact⁵) headed by septuple row of type orn.; C3<sup>v</sup> blank; C4 *Poems* section-title (verso blank); C5 dedicatory epistle (fact⁶) headed by orn. [as on A4]; C6<sup>v</sup> blank; C7 text of poems headed by quadruple row of type orn.; L8<sup>v</sup> orn. [figure with triang. scrollwork (46 x 52)]; M1 queen's pindaric ode section-title (verso blank); on O7<sup>v</sup> orn. [laced scrollwork with vines (31 x 59)]; O8 table of the poems.

RT] vol. 1: *The* OLD | BATCHELOUR. A7<sup>v</sup>-F7 [BATCHELOUR (no period) A8, C1, D1, E3, F3; *The* OLD BATCHELOUR. A8<sup>v</sup>]; *The* DOUBLE-DEALER. ²A7<sup>v</sup>-²G8 [DOUBLE-DEALEB. ²B4<sup>v</sup>]; *The* WAY *of the* WORLD. ³A5<sup>v</sup>-³H1 [WORLD: ³C8; WORLD (no period) ³F3, ³G3]; vol. 2: *LOVE for LOVE.* A7<sup>v</sup>-H7 [*LOVL for LOVE.* B6, D5, G6; *LOVE for LOVE,* F7]; *The* MOURNING BRIDE. ²A6<sup>v</sup>-²G1<sup>v</sup>; *The Judgment of* PARIS. ²G3<sup>v</sup>-²G6; vol. 3: *SEMELE.* A4<sup>v</sup>-C3 [*SEMELE* (no period) A6<sup>v</sup>, A7, A7<sup>v</sup>, B7, B8<sup>v</sup>]; *Poems upon ſeveral Occaſions.* C7<sup>v</sup>-O7<sup>v</sup> [ſerveral D3-D7<sup>v</sup>, E2-E3, E5<sup>v</sup>, F2<sup>v</sup>, F6<sup>v</sup>, F7, G1, G1<sup>v</sup>, G5, G6<sup>v</sup>, G7<sup>v</sup>, I6<sup>v</sup>, K8, M2<sup>v</sup>, N5; *Occaſion.* E7, E7<sup>v</sup>, G8<sup>v</sup>; *Poms* F5]

CW] *vol. 1:* ᵗA5 THE [ᵗA5ᵛ blank] B3 Heart. [Heart,] B8ᵛ *Aram.* [*Aram*] C2ᵛ Igad-[I-gad] C8ᵛ *Loining* [*Joining*] D7 *Læt.* [*Læt*] D8ᵛ *Bel.* [*Belin.*] E4ᵛ *Fond.* [*Fond*] ²A2 *Sudes* [*Sudet*] ³D7ᵛ Sir. [Sir] ³E8 ur [our] ³E8ᵛ *Milla.* [Mrs. *Fain.*] ³F8ᵛ *Wilfull* [*Willfull*] ³G3 amongst [amangst] *vol. 2:* B1ᵛ Sc- [SCENE] B5ᵛ *Vac.* [*Val.*] B8 *Frail.* [*Frail,*] D3ᵛ ACT. [ACT] E2 *Mifs.* [*Mifs*] E3 time [timi] F1 *Ang.* [SCENE] F3ᵛ Sir [Sit] G5 ACT. [ACT] H4 *Frail.* [*Frail*] ²A4ᵛ *Stil* [*Still*] *vol. 3:* A8 ACT. [ACT] B1 Scals [Scale] B5 JUNO. [JUNO,] C3 POEMS [C3ᵛ blank] C6 THE [C6ᵛ blank] D1ᵛ Stretch'd [Strech'd] E5 When [Wheu,] F3 *BA-* [*ABSENCE.*] G4 App'es [Apples] K7 A [As] L6 58 *The* [59 *The*] M2ᵛ (*Stan-*)*za's;* [*za's*] N4ᵛ Whe [What] [no cw on vol. 1: ²A5, ²A5ᵛ, ²A6, ²G3ᵛ, ²G7ᵛ, ³B4ᵛ, ³F3, ³F6ᵛ, ³H1ᵛ]

*Signing and numbering:* $5 signed (-*vol. 1* A5, B5, ²A5, ³F3, ³H3; *vol. 2:* A3). No press figures. Following errors in signatures: *vol. 1:* ³A6 signed ³A5; *vol. 3:* F3 signed L3. Following errors in pagination: *vol. 1:* p. ²15 misnumbered 19; p. ³79 misnumbered 97.

*Type and ornaments:* text (*vol. 1,* C6): 38 ll., 127(133) x 70 mm., 66 R. All acts of the plays and the opera are headed by a single or double row of type ornaments. Scenes in *MB, WW,* and *Semele* are headed by a single row of type orn. Scenes in *DD* are similarly headed up to Act IV, Scene 12 when the ornaments are omitted for lack of space. All commendatory poems, prologues, and epilogues begin with a 2-line cap. Poems which do not begin a page are headed by a rule.

*Notes:* This badly set edition is a Dutch forgery. All of volume 3 and *Judgment* from volume 2 have been reset from Tonson's 5th edition. The plays, individually paged and signed, were perhaps published separately (All of Congreve's plays are listed in Johnson's book advertisement, vol. 1, F8) and bound together to complete the edition. *The Old Bachelor* does not follow the scene division of the 1710 Tonson *Works; Love for Love* includes the anonymous prologue not included in the 1710 *Works;* three scenes in Act IV, *Way of the World* are misnumbered as 'II.' In volume 2 two ²G1's and ²G2's have been bound.

PR3360 .D52

## 115. 1753

[*General title*] as in 1730 (111.) except for | IN... | CONSISTING OF HIS | [1 line] || The SIXTH EDITION. || *LONDON:* | Printed for J. and R. TONSON and S. DRAPER | in the *Strand.* | [partial rule] | MDCCLIII.

[*vol. titles*] *vol. 1:* as in 1730 (111.) except for | *The* DOUBLE-DEALER. || [orn. T52] ||| *LONDON:* | Printed for J. and R. TONSON and | S. DRAPER in the *Strand.* | [partial rule] | MDCCLIII.

*vol. 2:* as in 1730 (111.) except for different ornament (T54) and imprint.

*vol. 3:* as in 1730 (111.) except for unseparated double rule and imprint.

*Section-titles:* as in 1730 (111.) except for the following: the different imprint date is regularly printed in arabic numbers and the imprint type is smaller on *MB, WW, Semele, Poems,* and queen's ode; *The Old Bachelor* and *The Double-Dealer* are in capitals; '*LOVE* for *LOVE.*' becomes 'LOVE *for* LOVE.'; the following section-titles have different ornaments as noted: *OB* (T54), *DD* (T52), *MB* (T52), *WW* (T75), *Semele* (T75), *Poems* (T75); the imprint date on *WW* s-t is printed as 7153; the spelling of 'PINDARIQUE' on the queen's ode s-t is 'PINDARIC' and 'Offer'd' is printed 'Off'd'; the Horatian motto on *DD* s-t is acknowledged as 'Hor. Ars Poet.'; *Judgment, Semele,* and *Poems* have 'Year' in imprint.

*Collation:* 12°. *vol. 1:* π1 A-M$^{12}$N$^6$, 151 leaves, pp. [26] *1–3* 4–125 *126–147* 148–272 *273–274* [2], plates [2] (opp. sigs. A6, G5); *vol. 2:* π1 A-M$^{12}$ χ1, 146 leaves, pp. [2] *1–13* 14–174 *175–187* 188–283 *284–286* [4], plates [2] (opp. sigs. A2, H5); *vol. 3:* π1 A-Q$^{12}$χ1, 194 leaves, pp. [2] *1–15* 16–147 *148–153* 154–159 *160–167* 168–197 *198–205* 206–336 *337–338* 339–365 *366* 367–382 *383–384* [2], plate (opp. sig. A2).

*Contents:* as in 1730 (111.) except for absence of concluding blank leaf in volume 1, different ornamental initials and factotums, and ornaments as follows: *vol. 1:* A3 T77; A5 T78 inverted; A7 T3; B1 T78; B2 T79 inverted; G3 T29; G4 orn. [scrollwork (15 x 33)]; G6 T79; H1 T80; H2 T81; N4$^v$ T52; N5 orn. as on G4. *vol. 2:* A3 T79; A7 T37, without border at top and sides (28 x 71); H3 fleuron; H6 T47; H9 T54; H10 T81; M11 T78 inverted. *vol. 3:* A3 T50; A8 T47; G3 T82; G5 T79 inverted; G10 T50; G11 T12; G12 T37, without border at top and sides; I3 T78; I5 T33, modified by removal of helmet and border (25 x 71); I7 T47; O12$^v$ T83; P5$^v$ T38 (Plomer 103); Q11$^v$ T82.

RT] as in 1730 (111.) except for the following variants instead of those in 111.: *vol. 2, LOVE* (no period), C10$^v$; *vol. 3, Poems on* K9$^v$, M9$^v$, P10$^v$, Q8$^v$.

CW] *vol. 1:* A5 THE [A5$^v$ blank] E7$^v$ Si [Sir] F1$^v$ SCEEN [SCENE] H3$^v$ *MEL. [MELLEFONT.]* M12$^v$ *MASK-[MASKWELL] vol. 2:* A12$^v$ *TRAP-[TRAPLAND.]* C5 *VA. [VALENTINE.]* E12$^v$ Face: L5 SCENE. [SCENE] *vol. 3:* C12$^v$ remove E1 Mrs. E11$^v$ *that* G3 THE [G3$^v$ blank] G8 SEME-[G8$^v$ blank] I3 POEMS [I3$^v$ blank] I6 THE [I6$^v$ blank] I11$^v$ Cla [Clamours] O7 5 *See* [5 *She*] P9 Nor [II. Nor] P10$^v$ Thus [II. Thus] P12$^v$ What

*Signing and numbering:* $5 (-*vol. 1*, N4.5; +*vol. 1*, G6, *vol. 2*, H6) signed. On

$1 of each signed gathering (except *vol. 3* sig. P1) in signature-line next fold 'VOL. I.' and according to volume with rom. numbers. No press figures.

*Type and ornaments:* text (*vol. 1*, B3): 35 ll., 122(132) x 73 mm., 70 R. Each act has a small headpiece, each scene is separated by a cast ornament, and each act of the plays and opera begins with a factotum (5–6 ll.) or ornamented initial (4–6 ll.). Each play is preceded by a disjunct engraving: all are signed on the left '*F. Hayman inv. et del.*' and on the right '*C. Grignion sculp.*' The *OB* engraving depicts the scene (III, 10) in which Sylvia spurns Heartwell's gold to make him propose. The engraved surface measures 126 x 76 mm. The *DD* engraving depicts the exposure of Lady Touchwood by her husband (V, 23); the engraved surface measures 128 x 78 mm. The *LL* engraving depicts Act IV, Scene VIII, where Sir Sampson shows Valentine the agreement he has signed earlier; the engraved surface measures 122 x 75 mm. The *MB* engraving depicts the emergence of Osmyn from the tomb to the startled Almeria and Leonora; the engraved surface measures 126 x 78 mm. The *WW* engraving depicts the appearance of the drunken Sir Wilful before the ladies (IV, 10); the engraved surface measures 126 x 76 mm.

*Notes:* Set from the 1730 edition, this edition differs obviously in the ornaments and the absence of press figures. Nearly identical page settings. The scene misnumberings of the 1730 edition have been corrected.

PR3360 .D53

## 116.  1761

[*General title*] THE | WORKS | OF | Mr. *WILLIAM  CONGREVE.* | IN THREE VOLUMES. | CONSISTING OF | His PLAYS and POEMS. | [type orn.: Baskerville 1] | *BIRMINGHAM,* | Printed by JOHN BASKERVILLE; | For J. and R. TONSON, in the *Strand, London.* | M DCC LXI.

[*vol. titles*] *vol. 1:* THE | WORKS | OF | Mr. *WILLIAM CONGREVE.* | VOLUME THE FIRST. | CONTAINING, | *The* OLD BATCHELOR, *a Comedy.* | *The* DOUBLE DEALER, *a Comedy.* | [orn. and imprint as on general title]. *vols. 2–3:* as in vol. 1 except for vol. no. and contents.

*Section-titles: vol. 1,* b1: THE | OLD BATCHELOR. | A | COMEDY. | [type orn.] | [4-line motto from Horace and 1-line ack.] | [type orn.] | Printed in the YEAR M DCC LXI. M4: THE | DOUBLE DEALER. | A | COMEDY. | [type orn.] | [1-line motto from Horace and 1-line ack.; 3-line motto from Terence and 1-line ack.] | [type orn.] | [imprint as on *OB* s-t]. *vol. 2,* A2: LOVE FOR LOVE. | A | COMEDY. | [type orn.] |

[2-line motto from Horace and ack.] | [type orn.] | [imprint as on *OB* s-t]. S4: THE | WAY of the WORLD. | A | COMEDY. | [type orn.] | [3-line motto from Horace and ack.] | [type orn.] | [imprint as on *OB* s-t]. *vol. 3*, A2: THE | MOURNING BRIDE. | A | TRAGEDY. | [type orn.] | [2-line motto from Ovid and 1-line ack.] | [type orn.] | [imprint as on *OB* s-t]. K6: THE | JUDGMENT | OF | PARIS. | A | MASQUE. | [type orn.] | [1-line motto from Ovid and 1-line ack.] | [type orn.] | [imprint as on *OB* s-t]. L4: *SEMELE.* | AN | OPERA. | [type orn.] | [3-line motto from Seneca and 1-line ack.] | [type orn.] | [imprint as on *OB* s-t]. O6: POEMS | UPON | SEVERAL OCCASIONS. | [type orn.] | [2-line motto from Horace and ack.] | [type orn.] | [imprint as on *OB* s-t]. 2D6: A | PINDARIC ODE, | Humbly offered to the | QUEEN, | On the Victorious Progreſs of | Her MAJESTY's Arms, | Under the Conduct of the | DUKE of *MARLBOROUGH.* | [type orn.] | To which is prefixed, | A DISCOURSE on the PINDARIC ODE. | [type orn.] | [2-line motto from Horace and ack.] | [type orn.] | [imprint as on *OB* s-t]. 2H7: A | LETTER | TO | Mr. DENNIS, | CONCERNING | HUMOR in COMEDY. | [type orn.] | [imprint as on *OB* s-t].

*Collation:* 8°. *vol. 1: A⁴* a-b⁸ B-Z⁸ 2A⁴, 200 leaves, pp. *i–ix* x–xxiv, [16] 1–164 *165–186* 187–358 *359–360*, plates [3] (opp. sigs. *A1*, b1, M4); *vol. 2: A²* a⁴ B-2I⁸ 2K², 256 leaves, pp. *1–12* 17–274 *275–294* 295–514 *515–516* [=512], plates [2] (opp. sigs. B1, S4); *vol. 3: A²* a⁴ B-2I⁸ 2K², 256 leaves, pp. *1–12* 17–151 *152–156* 157–166 *167–172* 173–217 *218–225* 226–426 *427–428* 429–492 *493–494* 495–514 *515–516* [=512], plate (opp. sig. B1).

*Contents: vol. 1: A1* title (verso blank); *A2* vol. title (verso blank); *A3* preface; a1 'THE | LIFE | OF | CONGREVE.' b1 *OB* s-t (verso blank); b2 dedicatory epistle; b4 Southerne's commendatory poem; b5 Marsh's commendatory poem; on b5ᵛ Higgons' commendatory poem; b6ᵛ Falkland's prologue; b7ᵛ prologue; b8ᵛ dramatis personae (with cast); B1 *OB* text with HT; M3 epilogue; M4 *DD* s-t (verso blank); M5 dedicatory epistle; N2 Dryden's commendatory poem; N4ᵛ prologue; N5ᵛ dramatis personae (with cast); N6 *DD* text with HT; 2A4 epilogue. *vol. 2: A1* vol. title (verso blank); *A2 LL* s-t (verso blank); a1 dedicatory epistle; a3 prologue; a4ᵛ dramatis personae (with cast); B1 *LL* text with HT; S2 epilogue; S3ᵛ blank; S4 *WW* s-t (verso blank); S5 dedicatory epistle; T1 Steele's commendatory poem; T2ᵛ prologue; T3ᵛ dramatis personae (with cast); T4 *WW* text with HT; 2K2 epilogue. *vol. 3: A1* vol. title (verso blank); *A2 MB* s-t (verso blank); a1 dedicatory epistle; a3 prologue; a4ᵛ dramatis personae (with cast); B1 *MB* text with HT; K4ᵛ epilogue; K5ᵛ blank; K6 *Judgment* s-t (verso blank); K7 *Judgment* text with HT; L4 *Semele* s-t (verso blank); L5 argument; L6ᵛ dramatis personae; L7 *Semele* text with HT; O5ᵛ blank; O6 *Poems* s-t (verso blank); O7 dedicatory epistle; O8ᵛ blank; P1 text of poems; 2D6 queen's pindaric s-t (verso blank); 2H7 letter on humour s-t (verso blank); 2H8 text of letter with HT; 2K2 table of the poems.

RT] *vol. 1: The* LIFE *of* CONGREVE. a1ᵛ-a8ᵛ; *The* OLD BATCHELOR. B1ᵛ-M2ᵛ; *The* DOUBLE DEALER. N6ᵛ-2A3ᵛ. *vol. 2:* LOVE *for* LOVE. B1ᵛ-S1ᵛ; *The* WAY *of the* WORLD. T4ᵛ-2K1ᵛ; *vol. 3: The* MOURNING BRIDE. B1ᵛ-K4 [BRIDE (no period) B6] *The* JUDGMENT *of* PARIS. K7ᵛ-L3ᵛ; SEMELE. L7ᵛ-O5; POEMS *upon ſeveral Occaſions.* P1ᵛ-2H6ᵛ; *Concerning* HUMOR *in Comedy.* 2H8ᵛ-2K1ᵛ.

CW] *vol. 1:* a8ᵛ THE G6ᵛ SHARPER. [SHARPER,] Z8ᵛ *Lady vol. 2:* a4ᵛ LOVE S3 THE [S3ᵛ blank] 2C4 *Mr.* [*Mrs.*] 2E4 (of-) fer, [fer?] *vol. 3:* a4ᵛ THE K5 THE [K5ᵛ blank] M7ᵛ 'Till [Till] M8 A [A] O5 POEMS O5ᵛ [blank] O8 THE [O8ᵛ blank] 2B8ᵛ Then, [Then] 2G1 The [*The*] [cw on 2E1 follows the notes rather than precedes.]

*Signing and numbering:* \$4 (-*vol. 1*, 2A3.4; *vol. 2*, a3.4, 2K2; *vol. 3*, a3.4, 2K2) signed. On \$1 of each signed gathering (except *vol. 1*, sig. Q and *vol. 3.*, sig. M) in signature-line next fold 'VOL. I.' and according to volume with rom. numbers. In gatherings B, C, D of *Vol. 3* the third Roman number has been imposed upon the period. No press figures.

*Type and ornaments:* text (*vol. 1*, B3): 29 ll., 155(167) x 87mm, 107 R. The preface, each dedicatory epistle, commendatory poem, prologue, and epilogue, and the life of Congreve, the argument to *Semele*, and the table of the poems is headed by a row of type orn. (Baskerville 1) and begins with a 2-line capital. Each HT is set off by a row of the same ornaments; acts and scenes and poems when they do not begin a page are headed by a row. All type ornaments in the edition are of this variety.[1] The edition has as a frontispiece a portrait of Congreve. The engraved surface, which measures 153 × 98 mm., is signed on the left '*G. Kneller Bart. pinxt.*' and on the right '*T. Chambars sculp.*' The title page of each play except *Love for Love* and *The Mourning Bride* is preceded by a disjunct Hayman-Grignion engraving; the plates precede the text of *Love for Love* and *The Mourning Bride*. Although the measurements may vary as much as a millimeter, the engravings are those of the 1753 *Works* (115.)

*Notes:* Gaskell 16. There are two cancel stubs between *A4* and a1 in vol. 1, one between *A2* and a1 in vol. 2, and one between *A2* and a1, vol. 3. The read-

---

[1] The Baskerville ornaments have frequently been reprinted. See Gaskell; Ralph Straus and Robert K. Dent, *John Baskerville: A Memoir* (Cambridge, 1907); and John Dreyfus, "Baskerville's Ornaments," *Transactions of the Cambridge Bibliographical Society*, I (1950), 173–177.

ings in the *A*, a, and b gatherings in vol. 1 conform to the pattern of the cancellantia described by Gaskell, p. 36.

PR3360 .D61

## 117. 1774

[No general title]
[*vol. titles*] *vol. 1:* THE | WORKS | OF | MR. CONGREVE: | IN TWO VOLUMES. | VOL. I. | CONTAINING | THE OLD BATCHELOR, | THE DOUBLE DEALER, | LOVE FOR LOVE. | THE SEVENTH EDITION. | To which is prefixed, | THE LIFE OF THE AUTHOR. | LONDON: | Printed for T. LOWNDES, T. CASLON, T. DAVIES, | W. NICOLL, S. BLADON, and R. SNAGG. | M DCC LXXIV. *vol. 2:* as in vol. 1 except for vol. number, contents list, and the omission of the reference to the prefixed life. The titles of the individual works (except *Semele*) are followed by periods rather than commas.

*Half-titles:* Each play, masque, and opera has a half-title, with the title (two lines except for *Love for Love* and *Semele*) followed by a colon (except *Love for Love*, *The Mourning Bride*, and *Semele* by a period, and *The Way of the World* by a comma) and the classification as comedy, tragedy, etc. (two lines) set in roman capitals. The mottoes, in italic, are those of the first edition except for *The Double-Dealer*, which follows the second edition and which misprints '*Corſilio*' for '*Conſilio*', and *Judgment* and *Semele*, which follow the 1710 *Works*. The *Poems*, the queen's pindaric ode, and 'Homer's Hymn to Venus' have half-titles; that of *Poems* following the motto of 1710 and the ode the first edition.

*Collation:* 12°. *vol. 1:* π1 A-O¹² P⁶ (P3.4 lacking) χ1, 174 leaves, pp. [2] *1–2* 3–8 *9–12* 13–21 *22* 23–106 *107–110* 111–121 *122* 123–214 *215–218* 219–225 *226* 227–339 *340* *345–348* [=344] [2], plate (opp. sig. A1); *vol. 2:* π1 A-R¹² S⁶ χ1, 212 leaves, pp. [2] *1–6* 7–11 *12* 13–82 *83–86* 87–95 *96* 97–196 *197–198* 199–205 *206–208* 209 *210–212* 213–239 *240–242* 243 *244* 245–370 *371–372* 373–398 *399–400* 401–419 *420* [2].

*Contents: vol. 1:* π1ʳ⁻ᵛ blank; A1 vol. title (verso blank); A2 [row of rectangles of fleurons] | 'THE | LIFE | OF | MR. CONGREVE.' [text cap²]; A5 blank; A5ᵛ *OB* engraving; A6 *OB* half-title (verso blank); A7 dedicatory epistle headed by row of star type orn.; A8ᵛ Southerne's commendatory poem headed by row of garland type orn.; A9ᵛ Marsh's commendatory poem; A10 Higgons' commendatory poem; A10ᵛ Falkland's prologue; A11 prologue; A11ᵛ dramatis personae (with cast); A12 *OB* text (cap²) headed by row of garland type orn., HT, and row of spider type orn.; E5ᵛ epilogue; E6 blank; E6ᵛ *DD* engraving; E7 *DD* half-title (verso blank); E8 dedicatory epistle headed by double row of garland type orn.; E11 Dryden's commendatory poem headed by row of garland type orn.; E12ᵛ prologue; F1ᵛ dramatis personae (with cast); F2 *DD* text (cap²) with type orn. setting off HT as on A12; I11 epilogue; I12 blank; I12ᵛ *LL* engraving; K1 *LL* half-title (verso blank); K2 dedicatory epistle headed by double row of garland type orn.; K3ᵛ prologue; K4ᵛ epilogue; K5ᵛ dramatis personae (with cast); K6 *LL* text (cap²) headed by orn. setting off HT as on A12; P2ᵛ 'BOOKS *printed for* T. LOWNDES.'; χ1ʳ⁻ᵛ blank. *vol. 2:* π1ʳ⁻ᵛ blank; A1 vol. title (verso blank); A2 blank; A2ᵛ *MB* engraving; A3 *MB* half-title (verso blank); A4 dedicatory epistle; A5ᵛ prologue; A6ᵛ dramatis personae (with cast); A7 *MB* text (cap³) headed by row of fleuron type orn. and row of spider type orn. setting off HT; D5 epilogue; D6 blank; D6ᵛ *WW* engraving; D7 *WW* half-title (verso blank); D8 dedicatory epistle; D10ᵛ Steele's commendatory poem; D11ᵛ prologue; D12ᵛ dramatis personae (with cast); E1 *WW* text (cap²) with type orn. setting off HT as on vol. 2, A7; I2 epilogue; I3 *Judgment* half-title (verso blank); I4 *Judgment* text (cap²) headed by HT set off by single rows of type orn.; I7ᵛ blank; I8 *Semele* half-title (verso blank); I9 argument; I10ᵛ dramatis personae; I11 *Semele* text (cap²) headed by HT set off by single rows of fleurons; K12ᵛ blank; L1 *Poems* half-title (verso blank); L2 dedicatory epistle; L3 text of *Poems* (cap²) headed by row of type orn.; Q6 queen's pindaric half-title (verso blank); R8 'Homer's Hymn' half-title (verso blank); S5 table of the poems; S6ᵛ blank; χ1ʳ⁻ᵛ blank.

RT] *vol. 1:* THE OLD BATCHELOR. A12ᵛ-E5 [BATCHELOR (no period) C4ᵛ, E2]; THE DOUBLE DEALER. F2ᵛ-I10ᵛ [DEALRR. I2]; LOVE FOR LOVE. K6ᵛ-P2. *vol. 2:* THE MOURNING BRIDE. A7ᵛ-D4ᵛ; THE WAY OF THE WORLD. E1ᵛ-I1ᵛ; THE JUDGMENT OF PARIS. I4ᵛ-I7 [JUDGMENT I6ᵛ]; SEMELE. I11ᵛ-K12; POEMS ON SEVERAL OCCASIONS. L3ᵛ-S4ᵛ.

CW] *vol. 1:* A4ᵛ THE (A5 blank) A9 TO (To] A9ᵛ TO [To] B11 witha [withal--] C5 *Shp.* [*Sharp.*] D11ᵛ *Sett.* [*Setter.*] E1ᵛ Boſom! -- [Boſom --] E5ᵛ THE [E6 blank] E8 *aboret* [*laboret*] H6 Lord [Lady] I4 *Maſk.* [*Maſkw.*] I11ᵛ LOVE [I12 blank] K5 DRA [DRAMATIS] K10 *Scan-* [*Scand*] O10 I mean, [I mean;] *vol. 2:* F12 *Then* [III. *Then*] G12 Candler [Chandler] H4 *Foible.* [*Foi.*] I6 *VENUS.* [*VENUS*] I11ᵛ He [Her] K9 *JUNO.* [*JUNO*] R3ᵛ Volt [Volta] S2ᵛ But ['But] [no cw on *vol. 2,* C9ᵛ, E9, K2ᵛ]

*Signing and numbering:* $6 (-*vol. 1,* P5.6; *vol. 2,* I3, S4.5.6; +*vol. 1,* E7) signed. Half-title pages (except *Mourning Bride* and *Judgment*) are numbered when they are within the first six leaves of the gathering. P. 228, vol. 2, is misnumbered 218; the page no. for pp. 221-2, vol. 2, has been torn out. On $1 of each signed gathering (except *vol. 1,* sig. E) in signature-line next fold 'VOL. I.' and according to volume with rom. numbers. The following press figures are present: *vol. 1:* B5ᵛ-2, C8-3, D12ᵛ-6, E1ᵛ-7, F4ᵛ-2, G12ᵛ-3, H1ᵛ-6, I7ᵛ-7, K12-3, L11ᵛ-5, M12-2, N1ᵛ-7, O11-3; P6-2; *vol. 2:* A7-1, A8-2, B5ᵛ-2, B7-1, C7-1, D8-1, D8ᵛ-2, E12ᵛ-1,

F7-1, F8-1, G1ᵛ-1, G6ᵛ-2, G12ᵛ-2, H1ᵛ-1, I5ᵛ-2, I12ᵛ-1, K7-1, K8-1, L7-1, L11ᵛ-1, M1ᵛ-3, N1ᵛ-1, N12ᵛ-1, O6ᵛ-2, O7ᵛ-1, P1ᵛ-2, P12ᵛ-2, Q12ᵛ-1, R2-3, R2ᵛ-3, S1ᵛ-3.

*Type and ornaments:* text (*vol. 1*, B1): 38 ll., 125(134) x 71 mm., 65 R. Each act of the plays and the opera is headed by a row of type orn. except *OB* III; *MB* II, III, V; *WW* II, IV; and *Semele* II; each poem which does not begin a page is headed by a row of type ornaments. Each dedicatory epistle, commendatory poem, prologue, and epilogue begins with a two-line capital. The disjunct frontispiece to the edition, a portrait of Congreve, signed on the left '*Sr. G. Kneller Pin.*' and on the right '*M. Vdr. Gucht Sculp.*' is similar to but not identical with the engraving in the 1733 *Dramatick Works.* The engraved surface measures 105 x 74 mm. The half-title to each play is preceded by the appropriate Hayman-Grignion engraving of the 1753 *Works* (115.).

*Notes:* The *OB* cast, with the exceptions of Packer and Palmer as Bellmour and Vainlove, is that of the October 24, 1753 performance (Stone, p. 180). The cast listed for the *DD* performed at Drury Lane on March 23, 1773 (Stone, p. 186). The *LL* cast is that of the CG performance on May 6, 1774 (Stone, p. 198). The *MB* cast is that of the November 13, 1773 DL performance. The *WW* cast is that of the March 15, 1774 DL performance. Scene VI, Act IV, *DD*, is misnumbered 'VII.' Scene IV, Act III, *Semele*, is misnumbered 'VI.'

PR3360 .D74

## 118. 1778

[*vol. titles*] *vol. 1:* THE | WORKS | OF | Mr. WILLIAM CONGREVE. | In TWO VOLUMES. ‖ VOL. I. ‖| LONDON: | Printed for the EDITOR, and ſold by J. WENMAN, No. 144, Fleet-ſtreet, | and all other Bookſellers in Great Britain and Ireland. | MDCCLXXVIII. *vol. 2:* [as in vol. 1 except for vol. no.]

*Half-title: vol. 1–2:* THE | WORKS | OF | Mr. WILLIAM CONGREVE.

*Section-titles: vol. 1,* A2: THE | OLD BACHELOR. | A | COMEDY. ‖ BY | Mr. WILLIAM CONGREVE. ‖ [4-line motto from Horace and 1-line ack.] ‖| LONDON: | [partial rule] | PRINTED IN THE YEAR 1775. χ1: THE | DOUBLE DEALER. | A | COMEDY. ‖ BY | Mr. WILLIAM CONGREVE. ‖| [imprint as on *OB* s-t] 2a1: LOVE for LOVE. | A | COMEDY. ‖ [2-line motto from Horace and 1-line ack.] ‖ BY | Mr. WILLIAM CONGREVE. ‖| [imprint as on *OB* s-t except for '1776.'] *2N1:* THE | MOURNING BRIDE. | A | TRAGEDY. ‖ [2-line motto from Ovid and 1-line ack.] ‖ BY | Mr. WILLIAM CONGREVE. ‖ [imprint as on *LL* s-t] *vol. 2,* A3:

THE | WAY of the WORLD. | A | COMEDY. || [3-line motto from Horace and ack.] || BY | Mr. WILLIAM CONGREVE. || [imprint as on *LL* s-t] N1: THE | JUDGMENT | OF | PARIS: | A | MASQUE. || BY | Mr. WILLIAM CONGREVE. || [1-line motto from Ovid and 1-line ack.] |||| LONDON: | PRINTED IN THE YEAR 1776. O1: SEMELE; | AN | OPERA. || BY | Mr. WILLIAM   CONGREVE. || [2-line motto from Seneca and 1-line ack.] |||| [imprint as on *Judgment* s-t] S1: POEMS | UPON | SEVERAL   OCCASIONS. || BY | Mr. WILLIAM CONGREVE. || [2-line motto from Horace and 1-line ack.] |||| [imprint as on *Judgment* s-t] 2L1: A | PINDARIQUE ODE, | [6 lines] | A DISCOURSE on the PINDARIQUE ODE. | [2-line motto from Horace and ack.] 2N4: HOMER's | HYMN | TO | VENUS. | TRANSLATED INTO | ENGLISH VERSE.

*Collation:* 8°. *vol. 1:* $A^4$ B-L$^4$ M$^2\chi^4$ N-Y$^4$Z$^2$ 2a$^4$ (2a3.4 lacking) 2A-2M$^4$ *2N*$^2$ 20-2X$^4$, 176 leaves, pp. [4] *i–ii* iii–iv $^2i$ ii–v *vi 7* 8–82 *83–84* [4] *85–91* 92–169 *170–172* [4] 177–272 *273–279* 280–339 *340* [=336], plates [4] opp. sigs. *A3*, $\chi$1, 2a1, *2N1*; *vol. 2:* $A^6$ B-2Q$^4$ 2R$^2$, 160 leaves, pp. [8] *1–7* 8–91 *92–95* 96–100 *101–103* 104 *105–106* 107–132 *133–135* 136 *137* 138–259 *260–262* 263–282 *283–284* 285–299 *300–301* 302–311 *312*, plate (opp. sig. *A3*).

*Contents: vol. 1: A1* vol. half-title (verso blank); *A2* vol. title (verso blank); *A3 OB* s-t (verso blank); *A4* dedicatory epistle headed by double rule; B1 Southerne's commendatory poem headed by double rule; on B1$^v$ Marsh's commendatory poem; on B2 Higgons' commendatory poem; B2$^v$ Falkland's prologue; B3 prologue; B3$^v$ dramatis personae (with cast); B4 *OB* text (cap$^3$) with HT; M2 epilogue (verso blank); $\chi$1 *DD* s-t (verso blank); $\chi$2 dedicatory epistle headed by double rule; $\chi$4 Dryden's commendatory poem; N1 prologue; N1$^v$ dramatis personae (with cast); N2 *DD* text (cap$^3$) with HT; Z1$^v$ blank; Z2 epilogue; 2a1 *LL* s-t (verso blank); 2a2 dedicatory epistle; [leaves 2a3.4 lacking] 2A1: *LL* text [beg. with Jeremy's speech 'Now heav'n of mercy continue the tax upon paper;']; *2N1 MB* s-t (verso blank); *2N2* dedicatory epistle; 2O1 prologue; on 2O1$^v$ dramatis personae (with cast); 2O2 *MB* text (cap$^3$) with HT; 2X4$^v$ epilogue. *vol. 2: A1* vol. half-title (verso blank); *A2* vol. title (verso blank); *A3 WW* s-t (verso blank); *A4* Steele's commendatory poem headed by double rule; *A5:* dedicatory epistle headed by double rule; B1 prologue; B1$^v$ dramatis personae (with cast); B2 *WW* text (cap$^2$) with HT; M4$^v$ epilogue; N1 *Judgment* s-t (verso blank); N2 *Judgment* text (cap$^2$); O1 *Semele* s-t (verso blank); O2 argument; O3 dramatis personae; O3$^v$ *Semele* text (cap$^2$) with HT; S1 *Poems* s-t (verso blank); S2 dedicatory epistle (cap$^3$) headed by double rule; S3 text of poems; 2L1 queen's pindaric ode s-t (verso blank); 2N4 'Homer's Hymn' s-t (verso blank); 2Q1 life of Congreve; 2Q4 Vol. I contents; 2R1 Vol. II contents.

RT] *vol. 1*: The OLD BACHELOR. B4$^v$-M1$^v$; The DOUBLE DEALER. N2$^v$-Z1 [DEALER: T3$^v$]; LOVE for LOVE. 2A1-2M4$^v$; The MOURNING BRIDE. 2O2$^v$-2X$^4$. *vol. 2*: The WAY of the WORLD. B2$^v$-M4; The JUDGMENT of PARIS. N2$^v$-N4$^v$; SEMELE. O4-R4$^v$; POEMS upon SEVERAL OCCASIONS. S3$^v$-2P4 [OCCASIONS, 2E2$^v$, 2O1$^v$]

CW] *vol. 1: A4$^v$* THE [To] I1 SHAR [SHARP.] I4$^v$ *She* [[*She*] R4$^v$ L. FROTH [[L. FROTH] S4$^v$ Sir PAUL: [Sir PAUL.] Z1 EPI-[Z1$^v$ blank] 2A4$^v$ (ʃha-)dow, [ʃhadow,] 2K2$^v$ ANG. [Ang.] 2M4$^v$ EPI-[followed by disjunct engraving] *vol. 2*: C2$^v$ MIR. [MIRA.] I3--I [--If] L4$^v$ *MIR.* [*MIRA.*] 2C2$^v$ *Phrygia.* [29 *Phrygia.*] 2D1$^v$ if [If] 2K4 A PIN- [2K4$^v$ blank] [no cw on vol. 1, P1$^v$]

*Signing and numbering:* \$2 (-vol. 1, M2, Z2; vol. 2, 2R2) signed. Vol. 2, p. 86, misprinted as 6, 184 as 4. On \$1 of each signed gathering plus *A1* in both volumes in signature-line next fold 'VOL. I.' and according to volume with rom. numbers. Press figures are present as follows: *vol. 1:* A4-3, B4$^v$-6, C4$^v$-6, D1$^v$-6, E2$^v$-3, F2$^v$-3, G1$^v$-3, H3-3, I4$^v$-3, K1$^v$-3, L1$^v$-3, $\chi^2$-4, N4-3, O3-3, P1$^v$-1, Q3$^v$-1, R1$^v$-1, S3$^v$-6, T4$^v$-3, U4-5, X3$^v$-3, Y2$^v$-1, 2A4-2, 2B3-3, 2C2$^v$-4, 2D3$^v$-1, 2E3$^v$-2, 2F2$^v$-1, 2G1$^v$-6, 2H4$^v$-7, 2I3-3, 2K1$^v$-1, 2L1$^v$-4, 2M3-2, 2O4-5, 2P4$^v$-1, 2Q1$^v$-1, 2R3-3, 2S1$^v$-2, 2T4$^v$-1, 2U1$^v$-3, 2X3-2; *vol. 2: A5*-2, B4-3, C2$^v$-1, D3$^v$-5, E4-1, F2$^v$-3, G4$^v$-1, H4-3, I4-1, K1$^v$-2, L2$^v$-1, M3-3, N3-1, O4-2, P4-3, Q2$^v$-4, R4-3, S3-3, T3$^v$-3, U2$^v$-4, X3$^v$-2, Y4-2, Z4$^v$-4, 2A4$^v$-3, 2B3-4, 2C4-1, 2D3-3, 2E4-1, 2F3$^v$-1, 2G2-4, 2H3$^v$-4, 2I4-3, 2K1$^v$-5, 2L3-2, 2M3$^v$-3, 2N1$^v$-4, 2O3$^v$-1, 2P3$^v$-2, 2Q1$^v$-1.

*Type and ornaments:* text (*vol. 1*, C4): 44 ll., 159(166) x 82 mm., 72 R. The headtitles of the plays, the masque, and the opera are set off by a double rule above and a single rule below. Each act of the plays and the opera, when it does not begin a page, is headed by a rule; acts II, IV of *OB*, though they begin a page, are headed by a double rule. Poems when they do not begin a page are headed by a rule, except 'Song.' on p. 172. The dedicatory epistles to the plays, commendatory poems, prologues, and epilogues begin with a 2-line cap. Each play title page is preceded by a skilful imitation of the Hayman-Grignion engravings. The disjunct illustrations are set within an elaborate frame; the measurements of the engraved surface vary from 156 to 159 mm. vertically and 96 to 102 horizontally.

*Notes:* Leaves M1.2 in vol. 1 are repeated; leaves 2a3.4 are lacking. The catchword on A4$^v$, vol. 1 suggests that the text of the play was to follow; the absence of the *LL* epilogue despite the catchword on 2M4$^v$ suggests that the epilogue was omitted because the end of the gathering had been reached. Act I, Scene XI, *LL* is misnumbered 'X.' and the error continues throughout the act; Scene III, Act IV is misnumbered 'II.' The edition follows the scene divisions of the Tonson *Works*.

PR3360 .D78

## 119. 1788

*[No general title]*
*[vol. titles] vol. 1:* as in 1774 Lowndes' *Works* (117.) except for... CONGREVE. | [3 lines] | ...BACHELOR. | ...DEALER. | [one line] | A NEW EDITION. | ORNAMENTED WITH COPPER-PLATES. | TO WHICH IS PREFIXED, | A LIFE| OF THE AUTHOR. | [partial rule] | *LONDON:* | Printed for W. LOWNDES; J. NICHOLLS; W. | NICOLL; S. BLADON; and J. BARKER. | MDCCLXXXVIII. *vol. 2:* as in *vol. 1:* except for volume number and contents and omission of reference to prefixed life.

*Half-titles:* as in 1774 *Works* (117.) except that on the *OB* half-title 'Horat.' is in roman capitals and on *WW* half-title 'WORLD' is followed by a period and the motto is in roman type. The error in the *DD* motto is repeated.

*Collation:* 12°. *Vol. 1:* a¹² (a1 lacking, blank?) b⁶ B-L¹² M¹⁰, 147 leaves, pp. *iii–v* vi–xxiv *xxv–xxvi* xxvii–xxxv *xxxvi* [=34] *1* 2–70 *71–74* 75–83 *84–85* 86–160 *161–163* 164–169 *170–171* 172–260, plates [7] (opp. sigs. a2, b1, D1ᵛ, E1, G4, I2, K11ᵛ); *vol. 2:* π1a⁴ A-B¹² C⁶ ²A¹²(²A1 lacking) ²B-²M¹² ²N⁶, 184 leaves, pp. *iii–vi* vii–xi *xii* [= 10] *1* 2–60; *²3–5* 6–8 *9* 10 *11–13* 14–91 *92–95* 96–99 *100–105* 106–124 *125–127* 128 *129* 130–249 *250–252* 253–278 *279–280* 281–299 *300* [= 298], plates [5] (opp. sigs. a1, A8, C4ᵛ, ²A2, ²B9ᵛ).

*Contents: vol. 1:* a2 vol. title (verso blank); a3 ||| 'THE | LIFE | OF | MR. CONGREVE.'; b1 *OB* half-title (verso blank); b2 dedicatory epistle; b3ᵛ Southerne's commendatory poem; b4ᵛ Marsh's commendatory poem; b5 Higgons' commendatory poem; b5ᵛ Falkland's prologue; b6 prologue; b6ᵛ dramatis personae (with cast) [printed vertically] B1: *OB* text (cap²) with HT; D12 epilogue (verso blank); E1 *DD* half-title (verso blank); E2 dedicatory epistle headed by double rule; E4ᵛ Dryden's commendatory poem; E6 prologue; E6ᵛ dramatis personae (with casts) [printed vertically]; E7 *DD* text (cap²) with HT; H8ᵛ epilogue; H9 *LL* half-title (verso blank); H10 dedicatory epistle headed by double rule; H11ᵛ prologue; H12ᵛ epilogue; I1ᵛ dramatis personae (with casts) [printed vertically]; I2 *LL* text (cap²) with HT; *vol. 2:* π1 vol. title (verso blank); a1 *MB* half-title (verso blank); a2 dedicatory epistle; a3ᵛ prologue; a4ᵛ dramatis personae (with casts) [printed vertically]; A1 *MB* text (cap²) with HT; C6ᵛ epilogue; ²A1 lacking; ²A2 *WW* half-title (verso blank); ²A3 dedicatory epistle; ²A5 Steele's commendatory poem; ²A6 prologue; ²A6ᵛ dramatis personae (with casts) [printed vertically]; ²A7 *WW* text (cap²) with HT; ²D10ᵛ epilogue; ²D11 *Judgment* half-title (verso blank); ²D12 *Judgment* text (cap²); ²E2ᵛ blank; ²E3

*Semele* half-title (verso blank); ²E4 argument; ²E4ᵛ dramatis personae; ²E5 *Semele* text (cap²) with HT; ²F3 *Poems* half-title (verso blank); ²F4 dedicatory epistle headed by double rule; ²F5 text of poems (cap²) headed by double rule; ²L5ᵛ blank; ²L6 queen's pindaric half-title (verso blank); ²M8 'Homer's Hymn' half-title (verso blank); ²N5 table of the poems; ²N6ᵛ 'Directions to the Binder.'

RT] *vol. 1:* THE LIFE OF | MR. CONGREVE. a3ᵛ-a12 [CONGREVE (no period) a9]; THE OLD BACHELOR. B1ᵛ-D11ᵛ; THE DOUBLE DEALER. E7ᵛ-H8; LOVE FOR LOVE. I2ᵛ-M10ᵛ; *vol. 2:* THE MOURNING BRIDE. A1ᵛ-C6 [BRIDE (no period) A2ᵛ]; THE WAY OF THE WORLD. ²A7ᵛ-²D10 [WORLD (no period) ²B3]; THE JUDGMENT OF PARIS. ²D12ᵛ-²E2; SEMELE. ²E5ᵛ-²F2ᵛ; POEMS ON SEVERAL OCCASIONS. ²F5ᵛ-²N4ᵛ [OCCASIONS (no period) ²G4, ²H4ᵛ, ²N4ᵛ; OCCASIONS: ²H6ᵛ]

CW] *vol. 1:* a9 nay [any] B12ᵛ Heartwell, [*Enter*] E6 DRA- [Dramatis] I1 DRA- [Dramatis] L12ᵛ *Val. vol. 2:* a4 DRAMATIS [Dramatis] C3ᵛ Or, [Or] ²H12ᵛ PRO- [PROLOGUE] ²M12 Bleſs'd ["Bleſs'd] ²N2 "Of ["Oft] [no cw on *vol. 1*, M6, M8ᵛ, M10; *vol. 2*, ²M6]

*Signing and numbering:* $6 (-*vol. 1:* b4.5.6, M6; *vol. 2:* a3.4, C4.5.6, ²F2, ²N4.5.6) signed. Half-title pages (except *OB*, *MB*, and *WW*) are numbered when they are within the first six leaves of a gathering. The page number on p. 119, vol. 2, is a two-digit number, perhaps '11'. On $1 of each signed gathering in signature-line next fold 'VOL. I.' and according to volume in rom. numbers. The following press figures are present: *vol. 1:* a5ᵛ-4, b3ᵛ-7, B8-4, B12ᵛ-1, C6ᵛ-4, C7ᵛ-3, D7ᵛ-2, E3ᵛ-1, F6ᵛ-1, G7ᵛ-2, H1ᵛ-3, H7-6, I5ᵛ-2, I7-3, K11ᵛ-7, L12-1, M9-2, M9ᵛ-3; *vol. 2:* A11-6, A12-4, B11ᵛ-2, C1ᵛ-7, ²A12-6, ²B12-6, ²C12-4, ²C12ᵛ-2, ²D5ᵛ-3, ²E7-1, ²E8-4, ²F12-5, ²G7ᵛ-6, ²H5ᵛ-1, ²I5ᵛ-2, ²K7ᵛ-4, ²L2ᵛ-2, ²M11ᵛ-2, ²N1ᵛ-7.

*Type and ornaments:* text (*vol. 1*, B3): 41 ll., 136(144) x 74 mm., 67 R. The acts of the plays and the opera are headed by a rule except when an act begins the page; poems are headed similarly. Each dedicatory epistle, commendatory poem, prologue, and epilogue, and each poem begins with a two-line capital. The engraved frontispiece is identical with the disjunct frontispiece of the 1774 Lowndes edition (117.). The Hayman-Grignion engravings are reproduced as disjunct leaves, preceding the appropriate half-title except for the *LL* engraving, which faces the text of the play (I2). The edition contains 6 other engravings: The first, facing D1ᵛ, vol. 1, depicts the scene from *OB* (IV, 22) in which Fondlewife (Foote) has discovered Bellmour disguised as Spintext. The engraved surface, within single rules, measures 130 x 86 mm., and is signed on the left '*T. J. Barralet ad viv. del.*' and on the right '*Walker Sculp.*' The imprint has been clipped. The second, facing G4, vol. 1, depicts the scene from *DD* (IV, 2) in which Careless (Palmer) kneels to win Lady Plyant (Mrs. Gardiner). The engraved surface, within single rules, measures 129 x 86 mm. and is signed on the left '*Dodd ad viv. del.*' and on the right '*Walker sculp*'. Below: '*Published*

*Aprl. 5. 1777 by T. Lowndes & Partners.'* The third, facing K11$^v$, vol. 1, depicts the *LL* scene (III, 7) in which Ben's (Wilson) first advances to Prue (Mrs. Mattocks) are rejected. The engraved surface measures 127 x 85 mm. and is signed on the left *'Edwards ad viv. del.'* and on the right *'B. Rarting Sculp.'* Below: *'Publiſh'd Nov. 30th. 1776. by T. Lowndes & Partners.'* The fourth, facing A8, vol. 2, depicts Garrick as Osmyn ascending from the tomb (*MB*, II, 6). The engraved surface measures 132 x 86 mm. and is signed on the left *'Iſaac Taylor del.'* and on the right *'W. Walker Sc.'* The fifth, facing C4$^v$, vol. 2, depicts Mrs. Siddons as Zara committing suicide (*MB*, V, 10). The engraved surface measures 129 x 84 mm., and is signed on the left *'Stedhard pinxt.'* and on the right *'Collier sc.'* Between the signatures: *'Publish'd May 5th. 1783 by T. & W. Lowndes.'* The last engraving, facing $^2$B9$^v$, vol. 2, depicts Mrs. Pitt as Lady Wishfort, demanding that Peg fill her cup with cherry brandy (*WW*, III, 3). The engraved surface measures 130 x 87 mm. and is signed on the left *'Dodd ad viv. del.'* and on the right *'Walker Sc.'* Between the signatures is *'Publiſh'd Octr. 26th. 1776. by T. Lowndes & Partners.'*

*Notes:* Leaf stubs are present between G9 and 10, and I11 and 12, vol. 1, and between A5 and 6, C4 and 5, and $^2$B3 and 4, vol. 2. That between C4 and 5, vol. 2, is clearly a binding stub; the others may be. The stubs are not present in 120., but collation of the relevant pages reveals no differences. The DL cast listed for the *OB* is that of the 1780–81 season (Avery, p. 181); the DL cast listed for the *OB* is that of the 1784–85 season; the CG cast is that of the March 19, 1782 performance except for Mrs. Kemble as Cynthia and Mrs. Pope as Lady Froth (Avery, pp. 186–7); the DL cast for *LL* is that of the October 15, 1787 performance except that Waldron is listed as playing both Foresight and Trapland; the CG cast bears little resemblance to that listed for the one relevant performance on January 28, 1786 (Avery, p. 199); the DL cast listed for *MB* is that of May 19, 1787, the CG that of October 30, 1786 (Avery, pp. 206–7); the DL cast listed for *WW* is that of the May 23, 1786 performance; the CG that of November 11, 1784 except for Mrs. Pitt as Lady Wishfort (Avery, pp. 215–6). Scene numbers change only with changes in setting.

PR3360 .D88

## 120.  1788

A different state.

*Collation:* 12°. *vol. 1:* a$^{12}$ (a$^1$ lacking, blank?) b$^6$ B-M$^{10}$χ$^1$ $^2$a$^4$ $^2$A-B$^{12}$ $^2$C$^6$, 182 leaves, pp. *iii–v* vi–xxiv *xxv–xxvi* xxvii–xxxv *xxxvi* [=34] *1* 2–70 *71–74* 75–83 *84–85* 86–160 *161–163* 164–169 *170–171* 172–260 $^2$*iii–vi* vii–xi *xii* [=10] $^2$*1* 2–60, plates [10] (opp. sigs. a2, b1, D2, E1, G4, I2, K11$^v$, $^2$a1, $^2$A8, $^2$C4$^v$); *vol. 2:* A-M$^{12}$N$^6$, 150 leaves, pp. *1–5* 6–8 *9* 10 *11–13*

14–91 *92–95* 96–99 *100–105* 106–124 *125–127* 128 *129* 130–249 *250–252* 253–278 *279–280* 281–299 *300*, plates [2] (opp. sigs. A2, B9).

*Notes: The Mourning Bride*, which is paged and signed separately as in 119., is bound with a volume two title page in volume 1 after *Love for Love*. Vol. 2 has a title page (the missing ²A1, vol. 2 of 119.?), apparently a cancellandum, which differs from the vol. 2 title of 119. in that *The Mourning Bride* is not included among the contents, the phrase 'TO WHICH IS PREFIXED, | THE LIFE OF THE AUTHOR.' is present, and the imprint date is 'MDCCLXXXVII.' The *OB* Barralet-Walker engraving faces D2, vol. 1; the *WW* Dodd-Walker engraving faces B9, vol. 2. Except for the absence of a press figure on vol. 2, E8 (²E8, 119.) the pages of the two copies are identical.

PR3360 .D88a

## Congreveana

Collier, Jeremy. *A Short View of the Immorality and Profaneness of the English Stage.* 1698

### 121.

[within double rules] A SHORT | VIEW | OF THE | Immorality and Profaneneſs | OF THE | 𝕰𝖓𝖌𝖑𝖎𝖘𝖍 𝕾𝖙𝖆𝖌𝖊: | Together with | The Senſe of Antiquity | upon this | *ARGUMENT.* ‖ By *JEREMY COLLIER*, M. A. ‖ 𝕿𝖍𝖊 𝕾𝖊𝖈𝖔𝖓𝖉 𝕰𝖉𝖎𝖙𝖎𝖔𝖓. ‖ London, Printed for 𝕾. 𝕶𝖊𝖇𝖑𝖊 at the *Turk's-Head* | in *Fleetſtreet*, 𝕹. 𝕾𝖆𝖗𝖊 at *Gray's-Inn-Gate*, | in *Holborn*, and 𝕳. 𝕳𝖎𝖓𝖉𝖒𝖆𝖗𝖘𝖍 against the | *Exchange* in *Cornhil*. 1698.

*Collation:* 8°. A-T⁸, 152 leaves, pp. [16] 1–288 [73 misnumbered as 37, 126 as 621, 142 as 242, 165 as 195, 196 as 206, 204 as 202], $4 (-A4) signed.

*Contents:* A1: title (verso blank). A2: ‖ ‖ 'THE | PREFACE.' (cap⁸). A4: ‖ ‖ 'THE | CONTENTS.' (cap²). On A7: '*ERRATA*.' A7ᵛ: 'Books Printed for *R. Sare* and *H. Hindmarſh*.' On A8: 'Books Printed for *S. Keble* at the *Turk's-* | *Head* in *Fleet-ſtreet*.' B1: ‖ ‖ 'THE | INTRODUCTION.' (cap⁴). B2: ‖ ‖ 'CHAP. I. | *The Immodeſty of the* Stage.' (cap²). E4ᵛ: ‖ ‖ 'CHAP. II. | *The Profaneſs of the* Stage.' (cap²). H1: ‖ ‖ 'CHAP. III. | *The Clergy abuſed by the* Stage.' (cap²). K6ᵛ: ‖ ‖ 'CHAP. IV. | *The Stage-Poets make their Principal Per-* | *ſons Vitious, and reward them at the* | *End of the Play.*' (cap²). N1: ‖ ‖ 'CHAP. V. | *Remarks upon* Amphytrion, King Arthur, | Don Quixote, *and the* Relapſe.' (cap²). Q5: ‖ ‖ 'CHAP. VI. | *The Opinion of the* Pagans, *of the* Church, | *and* State, *concerning the* Stage.' (cap²).

RT] 𝔗𝔥𝔢 𝔍𝔪𝔪𝔬𝔡𝔢𝔰𝔱𝔶 | 𝔬𝔣 𝔱𝔥𝔢 𝔖𝔱𝔞𝔤𝔢. B2ᵛ-E4; 𝔗𝔥𝔢 𝔓𝔯𝔬𝔣𝔞𝔫𝔢𝔫𝔢𝔰𝔰 | 𝔬𝔣 𝔱𝔥𝔢 𝔖𝔱𝔞𝔤𝔢. E4ᵛ-G8ᵛ [𝔓𝔯𝔬𝔣𝔞𝔫𝔢𝔰𝔰 E4ᵛ-E8ᵛ.]; 𝔗𝔥𝔢 ℭ𝔩𝔢𝔯𝔤𝔶 𝔄𝔟𝔲𝔰𝔢𝔡 | 𝔟𝔶 𝔱𝔥𝔢 𝔖𝔱𝔞𝔤𝔢. H1ᵛ-K6; 𝔍𝔪𝔪𝔬𝔯𝔞𝔩𝔦𝔱𝔶 ℭ𝔫𝔠𝔬𝔲𝔯𝔞𝔤𝔢𝔡 | 𝔟𝔶 𝔱𝔥𝔢 𝔖𝔱𝔞𝔤𝔢. K6ᵛ-M8ᵛ; 𝔎𝔢𝔪𝔞𝔯𝔨𝔰 𝔲𝔭𝔬𝔫 | 𝔄𝔪𝔭𝔥𝔦𝔱𝔯𝔦𝔬𝔫. N1ᵛ-N6 [𝔄𝔪𝔭𝔥𝔶𝔱𝔯𝔦𝔬𝔫. N3, N5]; 𝔎𝔢𝔪𝔞𝔯𝔨𝔰 𝔲𝔭𝔬𝔫 | 𝔎𝔦𝔫𝔤 𝔄𝔯𝔱𝔥𝔲𝔯. N6ᵛ-O2; 𝔎𝔢𝔪𝔞𝔯𝔨𝔰 𝔲𝔭𝔬𝔫 | 𝔇𝔬𝔫 𝔔𝔲𝔦𝔵𝔬𝔱𝔢. O2ᵛ-O8ᵛ [𝔔𝔲𝔦𝔵𝔬𝔱. O4, O7, O8, 𝔔𝔲𝔦𝔵𝔬𝔱 (no period) O6]; 𝔎𝔢𝔪𝔞𝔯𝔨𝔰 𝔲𝔭𝔬𝔫 | 𝔗𝔥𝔢 𝔎𝔢𝔩𝔞𝔭𝔰𝔢. P1ᵛ-Q4ᵛ [𝔎𝔥𝔢 P3]; 𝔗𝔥𝔢 𝔒𝔭𝔦𝔫𝔦𝔬𝔫 𝔬𝔣 𝔱𝔥𝔢 𝔓𝔞𝔤𝔞𝔫𝔰 | ℭ𝔬𝔫𝔠𝔢𝔯𝔫𝔦𝔫𝔤 𝔱𝔥𝔢 𝔖𝔱𝔞𝔤𝔢. Q5ᵛ-Q8; 𝔗𝔥𝔢 𝔒𝔭𝔦𝔫𝔦𝔬𝔫 𝔬𝔣 𝔱𝔥𝔢 𝔖𝔱𝔞𝔱𝔢 | ℭ𝔬𝔫𝔠𝔢𝔯𝔫𝔦𝔫𝔤 𝔱𝔥𝔢 𝔖𝔱𝔞𝔤𝔢. Q8ᵛ-R5, [𝔖𝔱𝔞𝔱𝔢. R4ᵛ]; 𝔗𝔥𝔢 𝔒𝔭𝔦𝔫𝔦𝔬𝔫 𝔬𝔣 𝔱𝔥𝔢 ℭ𝔥𝔲𝔯𝔠𝔥 | ℭ𝔬𝔫𝔠𝔢𝔯𝔫𝔦𝔫𝔤 𝔱𝔥𝔢 𝔖𝔱𝔞𝔤𝔢. R5ᵛ-T2 [ℭ𝔥𝔲𝔯𝔠𝔥. S3ᵛ, T1ᵛ]; 𝔗𝔥𝔢 ℭ𝔬𝔫𝔠𝔩𝔲𝔰𝔦𝔬𝔫. T2ᵛ-T8ᵛ.

CW] B8 mat- [matter] C5ᵛ ap- [approv'd] D8ᵛ Age, E5ᵛ (𝔓𝔞𝔯𝔩𝔦𝔞-) 𝔪𝔢𝔫𝔱; [𝔪𝔢𝔫𝔱,] F8ᵛ ſhould G4ᵛ 'He [He] H3ᵛ Pen [pen] I8ᵛ his K8ᵛ (other-) wiſe L8ᵛ 'we ['Knavery,] M8ᵛ CHAP. N8ᵛ You O1ᵛ (Wea-) ther, [ther.] P2 2dly [2ly.] Q8ᵛ and ['and] R8ᵛ (cen-) ſure [ſure] T1 when ['when] T1ᵛ a ['a] T4 exqui, [exquiſite,] [no cw on A7, A8, A8ᵛ, O5ᵛ, T7].

*Type:* text (B5): 31 ll. with mrg. nn., 142(154) x 74 (88) mm., 92 R.

*Notes:* Page numbers are in the head-line against the outer margin. The free end-paper in front and back is missing. Bound in brown leather. Wing C5264. Congreve possessed the first edition. See *Congreve* 100.

PN2047 .C6

# Settle, Elkanah. *A Defence of Dramatick Poetry.* 1698

## 122.

[within double rules] A | DEFENCE | OF | Dramatick Poetry: | BEING A | REVIEW | OF | Mr. *COLLIER*'s View | OF THE | Immorality and Profaneneſs of | the STAGE. ‖ *LONDON:* | Printed for *Eliz. Whitlock,* near *Sta-* | *tioner's Hall.* 1698.

*Half-title: A1* ‖ A | REVIEW | OF | Mr. Collier. ‖

*Collation:* 8°. A⁴ B-H⁸ I⁴, 64 leaves, pp. [8] 1–118 [2] [77 misnumbered as 67, 103 as 113], $4 (-H3, I3.4) signed.

*Contents: A1:* half-title (verso blank). *A2:* title (verso blank). *A3:* ‖ ‖ 'PREFACE.' (cap³). B1: text (cap⁴) headed by double rule. On H1ᵛ: ‖ *'The Remarks upon King* | Arthur *and* Amphi- | tyron *Examined.'* (cap²). I4ʳ⁻ᵛ blank.

CW] B1ᵛ to ["to] B4ᵛ (*Weſtmin-)ſter; [ſter.]* B8ᵛ (Tran-)ſlates: [ſlates;] C8ᵛ the D8v "of E8v to F8v I hope G7 Cor- [Corruption] H2v Not [[Not] H3v materiality [imateriality] H4v why ["why]

*Type:* text (B3): 31 ll., 143(153) x 79 mm., 92 R.

*Notes:* No head-title or running-title. Page numbers are centered in parentheses. On *A2*v has been pasted the bookplate of Algernon Capell, Earl of Essex, which bears the date 1701. Attributed by Halkett and Laing to Edward Filmer, but by Bateson (*Cambridge Bibliography of English Literature* [1940], II, 401) to Settle. Wing F905. Purchased from Maggs Brothers, London, in 1959. See *Congreve* 101.

PN2047 .C66

## Collier, Jeremy. *A Defence of the Short View of the Profaneness and Immorality of the English Stage*. 1699

123.

[within double rules] A | DEFENCE | OF THE | Short View | OF THE | Profaneneſs and Immorality | OF THE | English STAGE, *&c.* | Being a | REPLY | To Mr. *Congreve*'s Amendments, *&c.* | And to the | Vindication of the Author of the Relapſe. || By *Jeremy Collier*, M.A. || *Fortem animum præſtant rebus quas turpiter audent* | [to the right] Juven. Sat. 6. || *LONDON:* | Printed for **S. Keble** at the *Turks-head* in *Fleetſtreet*, | **R. Sare** at *Grays-Inn-gate*, and **H. Hindmarſh** | againſt the *Exchange* in *Cornhil*, 1699.

*Collation:* 8°. *A*² B-I⁸ K⁶, 72 leaves, pp. [4], 1–139 [140] [34 misnumbered as 18], $4 [E3 misprinting as E5] signed.

*Contents: A1:* title (verso blank). *A2:* 'To the READER.' (cap²). On *A2*v: 'ERRATA.' B1: || || 'AN | ANSWER | TO | Mr. *CONGREVE*'s | Amendments, *&c.*' (cap⁴) H1: || || 'A | REPLY | TO THE | Short Vindication | OF THE | *Relapſe* and the *Provok'd-Wife.*' (cap⁵) K6v: advertisement for Collier's books.

CW] B8v more C5v ſome- [ſomewhat] D3v (ex-) cepti- [ceptionable] E7 Mr. *Con-* [Mr. *Congreve*] F8v (Sub-)ject. G1 *Val.* [Val.] H1v L. *Brute,* [L. Brute,] I8v might K2 (Cha-)racter, [racter;] [no cw on A2v]

*Type:* text (C6): 31 ll. with mrg.nn., 143(153) x 73 (86) mm., 93 R.

*Notes:* No running titles. Page numbers are centered in the headline in parentheses. Bound in brown cloth. Wing C5248.

PN2047 .C63

Langbaine, Gerard. *The Lives and Characters of the English Dramatic Poets.* 1699

## 124.

[within double rules] THE | LIVES | AND | CHARACTERS | OF THE | *Engliſh Dramatick* POETS. | ALSO | An Exact ACCOUNT of all the PLAYS | that were ever yet Printed in the Eng- | liſh Tongue; their Double Titles, the | Places where Acted, the Dates when | Printed, and the Perſons to whom | Dedicated; with Remarks and Obſer- | vations on moſt of the ſaid Plays. || Firſt begun by Mr. *Langbain*, improv'd | and continued down to this Time, by | a Careful Hand. || *LONDON:* | Printed for *Tho. Leigh* at the *Peacock* againſt St. *Dunſtan's-* | *Church*, and *William Turner* at the *White Horſe*, | without *Temple-Bar.*

*Collation:* 8°. A-O⁸ (O8 missing, blank?), 111 leaves, pp. [16] 1–182 [24] [99 misprinting as 9], $4 (-O3) signed.

HT] ||| THE | Lives and Characters | OF THE | *Engliſh* Dramatick Poets: | WITH AN | ACCOUNT | OF ALL THE | PLAYS, | Printed to the Year, 1698. ||

*Contents:* A1: title (verso blank). A2: || || 'THE | Epiſtle Dedicatory, | TO | *CHARLES CÆSAR*, Eſq; | OF | Bonnington *in* Hertfordſhire.' (cap⁵). A5ᵛ: || || 'THE | PREFACE.' (cap⁵). A6ᵛ: || || 'THE | NAMES | OF THE | Known Authors.' (cap⁸) [in double columns]. A8ᵛ: || || 'ERRATA.' B1: HT with text (cap⁴). L4: || || 'SUPPOSED AUTHORS.' (cap⁵). L6ᵛ: || || 'UNKNOWN AUTHORS.' (cap⁵). M7: || || 'THE | APPENDIX.' (cap⁴). N4: || || 'AN | INDEX | OF | PLAYS, | Referring to the | AUTHORS.' (cap⁸) [in double columns]. O3ᵛ: || || 'BOOKS *Printed for, and Sold* | *by* Tho. Leigh, *at the* Pea- | cock *in* Fleet-ſtreet.' (cap²). O7: || || 'BOORS [stet] *Printed for, and Sold* | *by* William Turner, *at the* | White Horſe *without* Tem- | ple-Bar.' (cap²).

RT] *Known* AUTHORS. A [letter according to alphabetical entries of authors' last names] B1ᵛ-L3ᵛ [AUTHORS (large lower-case Roman 'u') $8; B. (etc. with period) B4–B7, B8, B8ᵛ; A. (instead of C) B8; B. (instead of C) B8ᵛ]; *Suppoſed* AUTHORS. L4ᵛ-L6; *Unknown AUTHORS.* C [letter according to alphabetical entries] L7-M6ᵛ [AUTHORS (large lower-case Roman 'u') L8, M4)]; *The* APPENDIX. M7ᵛ-N3ᵛ.

CW] A8ᵛ THE B8ᵛ *Ordinary,* C2 *Love's* [*Loves*] D6ᵛ *Ev'nings* [*Ev'ning's*] E2ᵛ E *Edw.* [E | *Edward*] E5ᵛ *King* [*A King*] E8ᵛ *The* [*Raging*] G1ᵛ *Venice,* [*Venice*] G4ᵛ M. *Lewis* [M | *Lewis*] H7 P. *John* [P | *John*] I8ᵛ *Romeo* K4 me ['me] L2

Dr. *Rob.* [Dr. *Robert*] L4ᵛ SUPPO- [is] M7 with [a] N1 *Mary* [Mrs. *Mary*] O1 *S* Sacrifice [*S.* | Sacrifice] O6ᵛ *BOOKS.* [*BOORS*]

*Type:* text (C4): 46 ll., 151(160) x 85 mm., 66 R.

*Notes:* The following symbols seem to function as press figures: A5ᵛ-†; L4-*; L4ᵛ-†; M7ᵛ-†; N7-† (inverted); N7ᵛ-†. Leaf L4 is carefully distinguished by these symbols and by asterisks against the page numbers; the text on L5 begins in the middle of an entry on an author known only as '*W.R.*' whereas L4ᵛ had ended an entry for 'S.H.'; these details and the incorrect cw suggest that the leaf is a cancellans, possibly the missing O8. A cancel stub is present between A7-8. The continuation is customarily attributed to Charles Gildon. Osborn notes that the title page exists in three different states (*John Dryden: Some Biographical Facts and Problems* [New York, 1940], p. 6n.). The Congreve entry on pp. 21–25 is the earliest biographical account of the dramatist. Bound in brown leather. Wing L375.

Z2014 .D7L2 1699

## *The Kit-Cats.* 1709

### 125.

THE | KIT-CATS, | A | POEM. ‖ To which is Added | The PICTURE, in Imitation of ANNACREON'S | BATHILLUS. As alſo the COQUET BEAUTY, | By the Right Honourable the Marquis of | *Normanby.* ‖ *Tantæ Molis erat.--* ‖ *LONDON*: | Printed and Sold by *H. Hills,* in *Black-fryars,* | near the Water-ſide. 1709.

*Collation:* 8°. A⁸, 8 leaves, pp. *1-2* 3–16, $4 (-A3) signed.

HT] ‖ ‖ THE | Kit-Cats, &c.

*Contents:* A1: title (verso blank). A2: HT with text (cap⁴). A7ᵛ: ‖ ‖ '*The* PICTURE: *In Imitation* | *of* Anacreon's Bathillus, *by the* | *Right Honourable the Marquis of* | Normanby.' (cap²). A8ᵛ: 'TO A | COQUET BEAUTY. | *By the ſame Author.*'

CW] A2 With [And] A8 *The* [To]

*Type:* text (A4): 37 ll., 156(165) x 89 mm., 82 R.

*Notes:* A mock-heroic panegyric of Jacob Tonson, Congreve's publisher, as Bocaj and of the literary success of the Kit-Cats, the poem is attributed to Sir

Richard Blackmore by Halkett and Laing. Page numbers are centered in parentheses in head line. Mounted in a pamphlet binder.

PR3318 .B5A74 1709

## Jacob, Giles. *The Poetical Register.* 1719–1720

## 126.

[*vol. titles*] *vol. 1:* THE | POETICAL REGISTER: | OR, THE | Lives and Characters | OF ALL THE | *ENGLISH* POETS. | With an Account of their | WRITINGS. ‖ *Adorned with curious Sculptures engra-* | *ven by the be∫t MASTERS.* ‖ Poets *have an undoubted Right to claim,* | *If not the* greate∫t, *the mo∫t* la∫ting *Name.* | [to right] Congreve. ‖ VOL. I. ‖ *LONDON:* | Printed, and Sold by *A. Bette∫worth, W. Taylor,* | and *J. Batley,* in *Paterno∫ter-Row; J. Wyat* | and *C. Rivington,* in St. *Paul's* Church-yard; | *E. Bell* and *W. Meadows,* in *Cornhill,* and | *J. Pemberton* and *J. Hooke* in *Fleet∫treet.* 1723. *vol. 2:* as in vol. 1 except for vol. no. and . . . *Sculptures,* . . . | [12 lines] | . . . *Meadows* in *Cornhill* . . . | . . . Hooke, . . .

*Collation:* 8°. *vol. 1:* A⁸ (lacking A1) a⁴ B-Y⁸ Z⁴ 2A⁴ 2B², 189 leaves, pp. [2] *i* ii–vii *viii* [12] *1* 2–280 *281* 282–302 *303* 304–334 *335–336* [20], plates [6] (opp. sigs. A2, B1, C1ᵛ, D5, I4ᵛ, P2ᵛ); *vol. 2:* A⁸ a⁸ B-Y⁸ Z⁴ χ¹; 189 leaves, pp. *i–iii* iv–xi *xii* xiii–xxvi [6] *1* 2–324 *325* 326–328 [8] 437–444 *445–446* [=338], plates [7] (opp. sigs. A1, C4, D3ᵛ, D4ᵛ, K8, L4ᵛ, P4ᵛ).

HT] *vol. 1:* [orn.: floral urn with birds and foliage, within border (38   x   87) | THE | *Poetical   Regi∫ter:* | OR,   THE | LIVES   *and* CHARACTERS | *of the* Engli∫h DRAMATICK | POETS. | [row of crown type orn.]; *vol. 2:* [orn.: squirrel with foliage, within border (22 x 86)] | THE | LIVES | AND | CHARACTERS | OF   THE | *ENGLISH* POETS. | [row of crown type orn.]

*Contents: vol. 1:* A1 lacking; A2 title (verso blank); A3 dedicatory epistle to Lord Lansdown headed by orn. [bust on pedestal with cornucopias, within border (29 x 89)]; A6ᵛ blank; A7 preface headed by quadruple row of type orn.; a1 names of the authors [in double columns] headed by quadruple row of type orn.; a4ᵛ blank; B1 HT with *Register* text (orn. initial⁵); on T4ᵛ orn. [a crude version of T32]; T5 register of modern dramatick poets headed by quadruple row of type orn.; on U7ᵛ orn. [as on T4ᵛ]; U8 register of anonymous plays headed by quadruple row of type orn.; Y7 addenda and corrigenda headed by row of type orn.; Y8ᵛ errata; Z1 index of plays [in double columns] headed by quadruple row of type orn. *vol. 2:* A1 title (verso blank); A2 dedicatory epistle to the Duke of Buckinghamshire headed by orn. [as in HT, vol. 2, B1]; A6$^v$ blank; A7 preface headed by orn. [book in circular frame with perched birds, within border (27 x 83)]; a1 introductory essay headed by orn. [flowers, horns, and foliage (18 x 72)]; a6 names of the authors [in double columns] headed by orn. [Parnassus with foliage (15 x 71)]; B1 HT with register text (fact$^4$); R2 account of the non-dramatic works of the dramatic poets headed by orn. [as on vol. 2, a1]; T8 register of modern English poets headed by orn. [as on vol. 2, a1]; X4 anonymous poems headed by orn. [as on vol. 2, a1]; Y3 addenda and corrigenda headed by row of type orn.; Y5 index of poems [in double columns] headed by orn. [as on vol. 2, A7]; Z1 continuation of poetical register headed by quadruple row of type orn.; χ$^1$ errata (verso blank).

RT] *vol. 1:* Lives *and* Characters *of the* | Engliſh DRAMATICK POETS. B1$^v$-T4$^v$; Modern DRAMATICK POETS. T5$^v$-U1; Lives *and* Characters *of the* | Modern DRAMATICK POETS. U1$^v$-U7$^v$; PLAYS *Written by Anonymous* AUTHORS. U8$^v$-Y6$^v$ [*Anonymouus* X4] *vol. 2: The* Lives *and* Characters *of the* | ENGLISH POETS. B1$^v$-T7$^v$ [Caracters B2$^v$, C2$^v$, D4$^v$]; *The* Lives *and* Characters *of the* | Modern ENGLISH POETS. T8$^v$-X3$^v$; POEMS *written by Anonymous* AUTHORS. X4$^v$-Y2$^v$; *The* Poetical Regiſter *Continu'd.* Z1$^v$-Z4$^v$ [*Continu'd* (no period) Z2; *Continu'd,* Z3].

CW] *vol. 1:* a3$^v$ T. Tate [T. TAte] B8 IX. *Round* [IX. *The Round*] H8$^v$ Like I8$^v$ WILLIAM [H. | WILLIAM] U8$^v$ XIX. X3 I. ED- [E. | I. EDWARD] Z1$^v$ B. *Ball* [B. *BAll*] 2A4 R. *Ra-* [R. *RAging*] 2A4$^v$ S. *Sa-* [S. *SAcrifice*] *vol. 2:* a8$^v$ THE B6$^v$ II. *Phar-* [II. PHARMACEUTRIA,] B8 (Admi-) ration, [ration.] B8$^v$ VI. *A* [IV. *A*] D1$^v$ SMEC- (I. SMECTYMNUUS.] D6 (Lite-) rature [ture.] D8$^v$ *Mr.* [*Mr*] F3$^v$ after- [aftewards] I8$^v$ *Robert* [*Mr. Robert*] M8$^v$ Mr. GEORGE [*Mr.* GEORGE] P5$^v$ *Mr.* [W. | *Mr.*] X1 Henry [S. | HENRY] X4 VII. *Art* [VII. *The*] Y3$^v$ *The* [He] [no cw on vol. 1, X1$^v$, X2$^v$, X3$^v$, X4$^v$, X5, X7$^v$, Y2$^v$, Y3$^v$, Y4, Y6, Y7]

*Signing and numbering:* \$4 (-vol. 1 a3.4, Y4, Z3.4, 2A3.4, 2B2; *vol. 2* Z3.4). No press figures, although in Vol. 1, C1$^v$, C2$^v$, D8, I8, K8$^v$, P7, X7.8 are marked with an asterisk in signature-line. Following errors in pagination: *vol. 1:* 334 misprinted as 433; *vol. 2:* xiii misnumbered as xii, 271 misprinted as 27 with terminal digit dropped.

*Type:* text (*vol. 1*, D7): 37 ll., 155(165) x 85 mm., 83 R.

*Notes:* Each volume has a disjunct frontispiece engraved by Vertue: that in vol. 1 has 6 oval portraits of Beaumont, Jonson, Fletcher, Otway, Dryden, and Wycherley surrounding a larger one of Shakespeare; that in vol. 2 has 4 oval portraits of Milton, Butler, Cowley, and Waller surrounding a larger one of Chaucer. The engraving facing sig. D5, vol. 1, is the Vander Gucht engraving of the Kneller portrait of Congreve. Five of what are apparently binding stubs of the engravings appear in vol. 1; four in vol. 2. Each entry in each of the poetical registers is headed by a row of type orn. The account of Congreve's dramatic career appears in vol. 1, pp. 41–46; that of his non-dramatic poetic career in vol. 2, pp. 248–250. Osborn has noted Congreve's influence on Giles Jacob, the compiler, who pays tribute to Congreve in the preface for advice about composing the work. One letter from Congreve to Jacobs survives (*Hodges*, no. 132). Both volumes have the bookplate of Lord Lilford.

PR691 .J3

## *Memoirs of the Life, Writings, and Amours of William Congreve*. 1730

## 127.

MEMOIRS | OF THE | *Life, Writings,* and *Amours* | OF | WILLIAM CONGREVE *Eſq*; | Interſperſed with | Miſcellaneous Eſſays, Letters, and | Characters, Written by Him. | ALSO | Some very Curious Memoirs of Mr. DRYDEN | and his FAMILY, with a Character of Him | and his Writings, by Mr. CONGREVE. ‖ Compiled from their reſpective Originals, | By *CHARLES WILSON Eſq*; ‖ *Poets* have an unqueſtion'd Right to claim, | If not the *Greateſt,* the *moſt Laſting Name.* | CONGREVE. ‖| *LONDON:* | Printed in the Year M.DCC.XXX. | (Price 5*s.*)

*Collation:* 8°. A-H⁸ ²A-²K⁸ ³B-³F⁴ (F4 lacking, blank?), 163 leaves, pp. *i–iii* iv–vii *viii* ix–xvi *1* 2–112, ²*1* 2–156 [4] ³1–38, plate (opp. sig. *A1*).

HT] ‖ ‖ *MEMOIRS,* &c.

*Contents:* A1: title (verso blank). A2: [orn.: oval bucolic scene with shepherd playing a lute under a tree, within rect. border; signed on the left '*L. Gupee Inv.*' and on the right '*M. Vdr. Gucht Sculp.*' (41 x 81)] 'To the Honourable | George Duckett *Eſq*; | One of the Commiſſioners of His | Majeſty's Revenue of Exciſe.' (orn. initial⁵). Signed on A4: 'CHA. WILSON.' A4ᵛ: blank. A5: [orn.: head with wings imposed on crossed branches, with sun on left and moon on right (27 x 79)] | 'PREFACE.' (orn. initial⁴). On A8ᵛ orn. [bird within frame (18 x 25)]. B1: HT with text (cap⁴). ²A1: ‖ ‖ '*MEMOIRS,* &c. | PART II'. (cap⁴). ²C5: ‖ ‖ 'AN | ESSAY | Concerning | HUMOUR *in* COMEDY. | To Mr. *D*****.' (cap³). ²D5ᵛ 'THE | HUMOURS of *Tunbridge-Wells,* | Deſcribed: | To the SAME.' (cap²). ²E3ᵛ: ‖ ‖ '*INCOGNITA:* | OR | LOVE    and    DUTY | Reconcil'd.' (cap²). ²K7: ‖ ‖ 'INDEX.' ³B1: ‖ ‖ 'A TRUE | COPY | OF THE | Laſt Will and Teſtament | of *William Congreve,* Eſq;' (cap²). ³B4: ‖ ‖ 'THE | Duplicate WILL    and    CODICIL.'    (cap²)    ³D1ᵛ: ‖ ‖ 'CHARACTERS | OF | Mr. *CONGREVE.*' (cap²). ³E1: ‖ ‖ 'VERSES | To the Right Honourable the | Lord

Viſcount *Cobham*. | *Of Improving the preſent Time.*' [86 ll. 'S²INCEREST Critic of my Proſe, or Rhime,]. On ³E3: orn. [seated cherub with birds on sides, signed 'F.H.' (48 × 63)]. ³E3ᵛ: ‖ ‖ 'THE TRUE | COPY | OF AN | AFFIDAVIT, | Made before one of His Majeſty's Ju- | ſtices of the Peace for the City of | *Weſtminſter.*' (cap²) ³F2: 'NEW BOOKS *Printed for* E. Curll | *in the* Strand.' ³F3ᵛ: 'The *Lives* and Laſt *Wills* and *Teſta-* | *ments* of the following Perſons.'

RT] *Memoirs of the Life of* | William Congreve, *Eſq*; B1ᵛ-²K6 [Congreve (no comma) F1- ²K6; RT reversed on E7ᵛ, E8; no RT ³A1-³F4ᵛ]

CW] A6ᵛ *me,* [*me;*] B8ᵛ To C8ᵛ naught; D8ᵛ I E1ᵛ very [glad] E5ᵛ *Whoreſon,* [*Whoeſon,*] E6 Charcter [Character] F8ᵛ the G2 In [Indeed!] ²A7ᵛ "ſays, ["ſays] ²B8ᵛ Be ²C8ᵛ of ²D8ᵛ The ²E8ᵛ his ²F8ᵛ they ²G1 his [Stirrups,] ²H8ᵛ but ²I8ᵛ 300 ²K4 *idle,* ["*idle,*] ³B2 All [ALL] ³C4ᵛ Mr. ³D4ᵛ VER- [VERSES] ³E4ᵛ and [no cw on A8ᵛ, H8ᵛ, ²D5, ²I4ᵛ, ²K6ᵛ, ²K8ᵛ, 3F1ᵛ]

*Signing and numbering:* $4 signed (-A3, ³B3.4, ³C3.4, ³D3.4, ³E3.4, ³F2.3). Following errors in pagination: xiii as iix, 43 as 34, 110 as 111, 111 as 110, ²138 as 139, 139 as 138. Page numbers are in the headline against the outer margin except for 62 and 63 and ²126 against the inner margin, ²1 centered in parentheses, and all in the third numbering centered in parentheses. Press figures are present as follows: F7-1, G7ᵛ-1, H6-3, ²A1ᵛ-1, ²B7ᵛ-1, ²C3ᵛ-3, ²D1ᵛ-2, ²E2ᵛ-1, ²F5-3, ²G2ᵛ-3, ²H1ᵛ-3, ²I5-3.

*Type: Memoirs* (²A2): 31 ll., 144(154) x 81 mm., 93 R; will (³C3ᵛ): 21 ll., 135(150) x 79 mm., 129 R.

*Notes:* A leaf stub remains between A8 and B1. Ralph Straus (*The Unspeakable Curll*, p. 139) asserts that the *Memoirs*, though bearing a 1730 imprint, appeared in August, 1729 and that Charles Wilson was a pseudonym for John Oldmixon, a hackwriter for Edmund Curll (p. 290). The frontispiece is the Vander Gucht engraving from the Kneller portrait of Congreve; the engraved surface measures 95 x 74 mm. Bound in brown calf.

PR3366 .W5 1730

## 128.

THE | Temple of Fame, | A | POEM | OCCASION'D | By the Late ſucceſs of the *Duke* of *Ormond,* the *Duke* | of *Marlborough,* Sir *George Rook* &c. Againſt | *France* and *Spain.* ‖ Inſcrib'd to Mr. *CONGREVE.* ‖ *Per Graium populos Mediæq; per Elidis urbem,* | *Ibat ovans Divumq; ſibi poſcebat Honores.* ‖ *LONDON,* | Printed for *JOHN NUTT,* near *Stationers-* | *Hall,* 1703.

*Collation:* 2°. *A*² B-C² (C2 lacking, blank?) D², 7 leaves, pp. [*2*] 1–12 [misprinting 6 as 9], $1 signed.

HT] ‖ ‖ THE | Temple      of      Fame, | INSCRIB'D      TO | Mr*
*CONGREVE.*

*Contents: A1:* title (verso blank). *A2:* HT with text. On D²: ‖ *'FINIS.'* ‖

CW] A2ᵛ Averſe B2 Ci -[Cities] C1ᵛ There

*Type:* text (B1ᵛ): 34 ll., 246(262) x 144 mm., 145 R.

*Notes:* No RT. Page numbers are centered in parentheses. Attributed to Thomas Yalden by Halkett and Laing. Bound in pamphlet binder.

PR3779 .Y28T4 1703

# APPENDIX A

ORNAMENTS USED BY TONSON IN HIS EDITIONS
OF CONGREVE.

1. This device Tonson used frequently on title pages of duodecimos of the plays designed to be sold separately and bound together.

2. headpiece: centered figures supporting a basket, with vines and scrollwork; no border (24 x 74 mm.).

3. headpiece: centered flower in oval frame, within medallion; cornucopia on each side; no border (25 x 73 mm.).

4. tailpiece: within border of scrollwork and musical instruments nude figures with horns have a music book between them (30 x 50 mm.).

5. headpiece: centered dog with ribbons around his neck, urn and foliage on each side; within rectangular border made up of small circles (24 x 73 mm.).

6. headpiece: centered urn with winged female figures facing opposite directions, bird on each side, within border ornamented with crosses (26 x 73 mm.).

7. tailpiece: a cherub on each side of a phoenix fanning with its wings the fire which consumes it; above, 'RENOVANT INCENDIA NIDOS' (40 x 53 mm.).

8. headpiece: centered phoenix on flames with scrollwork and cornucopias at sides (11 x 73 mm.).

9. tailpiece: garland of flowers with ribbons (16 x 35 mm.).

10. device: flowers in urn with leaves and single pendant flower on either side (13 x 33 mm.).

11. headpiece: centered flower with scrollwork, leaves, and flowers on both sides; no border (22 x 135 mm.).

121

12.

13. tailpiece: head with halo above a lyre with crossed horns in front and foliage on sides (19 x 38 mm.).

14. tailpiece: floral basket surrounded by vines (37 x 47 mm.).

15. device: three flowers with foliage (31 x 39 mm.).

16. headpiece: centered flowers with vines, within border (27 x 91 mm.).

17. headpiece: centered bust on lyre-shaped pedestal with vines running from cherubs at sides; within ornamented border (27 x 86 mm.).

18. headpiece: two cherubs centered supporting a basket, with vines; within border (28 x 90 mm.).

19. headpiece: centered owl with wings spread, on a book; vines and stylized dragons at sides; within ornamented border (26 x 85 mm.).

20. tailpiece: bird on pedestal within vine-entwined frame (49 x 63 mm.).

21. tailpiece: lamp on base with foliage (58 x 56 mm.).

22. tailpiece: cherub describing an arc on a globe with a compass, flowers on both sides (48 x 60 mm.).

23. tailpiece: centered flowers with flowers on sides (46 x 67 mm.), frequently inverted.

24. device: cornucopias crossed in front of a wheel, with foliage (15 x 45 mm.).

25. device: centered bouquet with single upright flower on left (13 x 33 mm.).

26.

27. tailpiece: illuminated head in elaborate medallion (30 x 51 mm.).

28. headpiece: ships entering a harbor, within border (27 x 72 mm.).

29. tailpiece: angel in a cloud with palm branch blowing trumpet (40 x 49 mm.).

30. headpiece: Neptune in a chariot, with nymphs; within border (27 x 72 mm.).

31. tailpiece: tree with birds (34 x 32 mm.).

32.

33. headpiece: centered armor with angels and battle flags; plumes on the helmet cause bulge in the border; sometimes without helmet (27 x 72 mm.).

34. headpiece: cupids heating arrows in front of a fountain; border broken at top right. (25 x 72 mm.).

35. tailpiece: Roman equestrian statue on pedestal, with flags (52 x 47 mm.).

36. headpiece: seated artist sketching ruined temple, within border (27 x 72 mm.).

37.                                        This headpiece was frequently used without the border.

38. tailpiece: cherubs holding portrait on pedestal, flowers (46 x 52 mm.). Reproduced as Plomer 103.

39. headpiece: mask with quills in elaborately ornamented border (23 x 75 mm.).

40. tailpiece: centered floral pedestal with urns on sides (35 x 55 mm.).

41. device: centered bouquet with pendants on scrollwork on sides (12 x 33 mm.).

42. tailpiece: bird with wings spread, on scrollwork (13 x 33 mm.).

43.

44. tailpiece: floral urn with vines (37 x 71 mm.).

45. headpiece: centered urn with foliage and birds at sides; no border (25 x 75 mm.).

46. headpiece: centered steaming urn with birds and foliage at sides (25 x 75 mm.).

47.

48. headpiece: centered tragic mask with pendant bouquets and scrollwork on sides; unbalanced; no border (25 x 74 mm.).

49. tailpiece: bust with bow and quiver on pedestal, within scrollwork (37 x 72 mm.).

50. headpiece: floral tray with foliage and birds; within border (23 x 74 mm.).

51. tailpiece: goddess on a boat drawn by birds, foliage and scrollwork at sides (42 x 64 mm.).

52. device: floral urn upon pedestal (14 x 34 mm.).

53. device: centered hare on pedestal, with scrollwork (14 x 33 mm.).

54. device: interlaced scrollwork (13 x 33 mm.).

55. tailpiece: single flower with vines and scrollwork (13 x 35 mm.).

56.

57. tailpiece: floral urn (27 x 45 mm.).

58. tailpiece: bouquet with birds (28 x 38 mm.).

59. tailpiece: centered armor with angels, battle flags, and cornucopias at sides (28 x 67 mm.).

60. tailpiece: oval framed picture of seated figure with lyre, head illuminated (36 x 55 mm.).

61.

62. tailpiece: mask with scrollwork (11 x 32 mm.).

63. headpiece: flowers, birds, and vines (7 x 73 mm.).

64. headpiece: centered cherub's head with cornucopias and flowers (6 x 73 mm.).

65. headpiece: centered floral basket with swans and vines (6 x 73 mm.).

66. headpiece: illuminated mask with scrollwork (6 x 74 mm.).

67. headpiece: entwined cornucopias with vines (6 x 73 mm.).

68. tailpiece: female figure in foliage frame supporting floral urn (25 x 26 mm.).

69. headpiece: encircled head with rampant lions and vines on sides (10 x 72 mm.).

70. headpiece: centered Holy Spirit as dove with cornucopias (18 x 73 mm.).

71. tailpiece: scrollwork (16 x 34 mm.).

72. headpiece: centered fountain with birds at sides; no border (19 x 74 mm.).

73. tailpiece: illuminated mask with cornucopias (18 x 28 mm.).

74. tailpiece: bouquet with vines (16 x 35 mm.).

75. device: interlaced scrollwork with pendants (13 x 33 mm.).

76. device: branched flowering vine (13 x 33 mm.).

77. headpiece: wave with lyre, books, horn, and caduceus (25 x 71 mm.).

78. tailpiece: flowers and leaves on elaborate tripartite base (35 x 38 mm.), frequently inverted.

79. headpiece: serpentine forms with garlands imposed upon irregular shell; no border (26 x 73 mm.), frequently inverted.

80. tailpiece: three flowers centered, with birds (23 x 46 mm.).

81. headpiece: palm-like tree and scrollwork, imposed upon irregular shell, supporting roof; no border (26 x 73 mm.).

82. tailpiece: floral urn (21 x 35 mm.).

83. tailpiece: centered bouquet with birds at sides (42 x 69 mm.).

84. headpiece: three plumes centered, with flowers and foliage (10 x 66 mm.).

85. headpiece: centered medallion of laurel-wreathed head, with shells; no border (25 x 70 mm.).

86. headpiece: crowned jester's head with seated angels at sides (9 x 73 mm.).

87. tailpiece: plume-like foliage (9 x 34 mm.).

# APPENDIX B

## TITLES IN THE HODGES COLLECTION WHICH DUPLICATE ITEMS IN CONGREVE'S LIBRARY

ARISTOPHANES.
[in black and red] COMEDIES | GRECQUES | D'ARISTOPHANE. | TRADUITES EN FRANÇOIS, | *AVEC* | Des notes Critiques, & un Examen de chaque | Piece ſelon les regles du Theatre. | *Par Madame DACIER.* | [orn. (23 x 35): flowers in a basket] | A PARIS, | Chez | [3 lines braced to left] DENYS THIERRY, Ruë S. Jaques. | ET | CLAUDE BARBIN, Au Palais. || M. DC. XCII. | *AVEC PRIVILEGE DU ROY.*
*Notes:* 12°. *Congreve* 192.
PA3878 .F7 1692

BALZAC, JEAN LOUIS GUEZ DE.
Balzac, Jean Louis Guez de. *Le Prince.* Paris, chez Toussaint du Bray, Pierre Roccolet, et Claude Sonnius, 1631.
*Notes:* 4°. The title page is engraved. *Congreve* 56.
DC123 .B3 1631

BEAUMONT, FRANCIS, AND JOHN FLETCHER.
[within double rules] FIFTY | COMEDIES | AND | TRAGEDIES. | Written by | [3 lines braced to right and left] FRANCIS BEAUMONT | AND | JOHN FLETCHER, | Gentlemen. || All in one Volume. || Publiſhed by the Authors Original Copies, the Songs | to each Play being added. || *Si quid habent veri Vatum præſagia, vivam.* || [a double row of six fleurons arranged vertically on either side of an orn. (McKerrow 317)] |||| *LONDON,* | Printed by *J. Macock,* for *John Martyn, Henry Herringman,* | *Richard Marriot,* M DC LXXIX.
*Note:* 2°. Wing B1582; Pforzheimer 54; *Congreve* 42.
PR2420 1679

BOCCALINI, TRAJANO.
[within double rules] *I RAGGUAGLI DI PARNASSO:* | OR, | ADVERTISEMENTS | FROM | PARNASSUS: || *In Two Centuries.*

|| WITH   THE | Politick   Touch∫tone. || Written   Originally   in ITALIAN | By  that  famous  ROMAN | *TRAJANO  BOCALINI.* || And now put into ENGLISH | By the Right Honourable, HENRY Earl of MONMOUTH. || *The Second Edition.* || *LONDON,* | Printed for *T. Dring, J. Starkey* and *T. Ba∫∫et,* and are | to be ∫old at their Shops in *Fleet∫treet,* MDCLXIX [with rule above date].

*Notes:* Wing B3382. Congreve had the first edition (1652). See *Congreve* 43.

JC158 .B7 1669

BURNET, THOMAS.

[within   double   rules]   THE | THEORY | OF   THE | EARTH: | Containing an Account | OF THE | 𝔒riginal of t𝔥e 𝔈art𝔥, | AND OF ALL   THE | GENERAL   CHANGES | Which   it   hath   already undergone, | OR | IS TO UNDERGO, | Till the CONSUMMATION of all Things. || THE  TWO  FIRST  BOOKS | *Concerning  The DELUGE,* | AND | *Concerning   PARADISE.* || *LONDON,* | Printed by *R. Norton,* for *Walter Kettilby,* at the Bi∫hops- | Head in S. *Paul's* Church-Yard, 1684.

*Notes:* 4°. Wing B5950; *Congreve* 41. Hodges incorrectly lists it as a folio as Congreve had done.

BL224 .B82 1690 v. 1

BURNET, THOMAS.

as in the preceding item except for | THE TWO LAST BOOKS, | *Concerning the* BURNING *of the* WORLD, | AND | *Concerning the* NEW HEAVENS and NEW EARTH. ||| *LONDON,* | Printed by *R. Norton,* for *Walter Kettilby,* at the Bi∫hop's | Head in St. *Paul's* Church-Yard. 1690.

*Notes:* 4°. Wing B5954. Although the item is not separately listed in *Congreve,* Congreve had listed *The Theory of the Earth* in two volumes (*Congreve* 41). Hodges speculated in his manuscript notes that Congreve had both of these items.

BL224 .B82 1690 v. 2

CATULLUS.

CATULLI, | TIBULLI, | ET | PROPERTII | OPERA | *Ad optimorum Exemplarium* | *fidem recen∫ita.* | *Acce∫∫erunt* | VARIÆ LECTIONES, | Quæ in Libris MSS. & Eruditorum Commentariis | notatu digniores occurrunt. || *CANTABRIGIÆ,* | TYPIS   ACADEMICIS, | Impen∫is JACOBI TONSON Bibliopolæ LONDIN. | MDCCII.

*Notes:* 4°. *Congreve* 91. Bears the bookplates of Gower Earl Gower and Bridgewater Library.

PA6274 .A2 1702.

## CHARDIN, JOHN.

[within double rules] THE | TRAVELS | OF | Sir John Chardin | INTO | 𝔓erſia anb tꙮe 𝔈aſt=𝔍nbieſ. ‖ The Firſt Volume, | Containing the Author's Voyage from *Paris* to *Iſpahan.* ‖ To which is added, | The Coronation of this Preſent KING | of Perſia, SOLYMAN the Third. ‖ [orn. (74 x 68): angel blowing a trumpet] ‖ *LONDON:* | Printed for *Moſes Pitt* in *Duke-Street Weſtminſter.* 1686.

*Notes:* 2°. Wing C2043; *Congreve* 81.

DS257 .C5

## DACIER, ANDRÉ.

[within double rules] THE | LIFE of *Pythagoras,* | WITH HIS | Symbols and Golden Verſes. | Together with the | LIFE of *HIEROCLES,* | AND HIS | Commentaries upon the VERSES. | Collected out of the Choiceſt Manuſcripts, and | Tranſlated into *French,* with Annotations. ‖ By M. *DACIER.* ‖ Now done into *ENGLISH.* ‖ The GOLDEN VERSES Tranſlated from the *Greek* | by *N. ROWE,* Eſq; ‖ [orn. (36 mm. diameter): within a double circle Pythagoras seated and around the margin 'ΠΥΘΑΓΟΡΗC CAMIΩN'] ‖ *LONDON,* Printed for *Jacob Tonſon,* within | *Grays-Inn* Gate next *Grays-Inn* Lane. 1707.

*Notes:* 8°. *Congreve* 365.

B243 .D2

## DRYDEN, JOHN.

OF | Dramatick Poeſie, | AN | ESSAY. ‖ By JOHN DREYDEN, | Servant To His MAJESTY. ‖ — *Fungar vice cotis, acutum* | *Reddere quæ ferrum valet, exors ipſa ſecandi.* | Horat. De Arte Poet. ‖ ‖ *LONDON,* | Printed for *Henry Herringman,* at the Sign of the *Anchor* on | the Lower-Walk of the *New-Exchange.* 1684.

*Notes:* 4°. Wing D2328. Macdonald 127bi. *Congreve* 171. Purchased from Maggs Brothers, London, 1959.

PN1631 .D7 1684

## HÉDELIN, FRANÇOIS.

[within double rules] THE | Whole ART | OF THE | STAGE. | CONTAINING | Not only the Rules of the *Drammatick Art,* but | many curious Obſervations about it. | Which may be of great uſe to the Authors, Actors, | and Spectators of Plays. | Together with much Critical Learning about the | Stage and Plays of the Antients. || Written in French by the command of | Cardinal *Richelieu*. | By Monſieur *Hedelin*, Abbot of *Aubignac*, and now | made Engliſh. || *LONDON*, | Printed for the Author, and ſold by *William Cadman* at the | *Pope's-Head* in the *New Exchange*; *Rich. Bentley*, in *Ruſſel-* | *ſtreet, Covent-Garden*; *Sam. Smith* at the *Prince's Arms* in | St. *Paul's* Church-Yard; & *T. Fox* in *Weſtminſter-Hall*. 1684.

*Notes:* 4°. Wing A4185; *Congreve* 10. Purchased from Maggs Brothers, London, in 1959.

PN1660 .A8

HOLYDAY, BARTEN.

[in black and red; within double rules] Decimus Junius Juvenalis, | AND | Aulus      Perſius      Flaccus | TRANSLATED | AND | ILLUSTRATED, | As well with | Sculpture as Notes. || By *BARTEN HOLYDAY*, D.D. | and late Arch-Deacon of *Oxon*. || [orn. similar to McKerrow 179 and 378 but without initials and with branches angled] || *OXFORD*, | Printed by *W. Downing*, for *F. Oxlad* Senior, *J. Adams*, and | *F. Oxlad* Junior. *Anno Dom*. 1673.

*Notes:* 4°. Wing J1276; *Congreve* 337. Has the bookplate of Samuel Treat Armstrong.

PA6447 .E5H7

JONSON, BEN.

[within double rules] THE | WORKS | OF | BEN JONSON, | Which were formerly Printed in Two Volumes, | are now Reprinted in One. | To which is added | A COMEDY, | CALLED THE | NEW INN. || With Additions never before Publiſhed. || — *neque, me ut miretur turba laboro*: | *Contentus paucis lectoribus*. || [orn: similar to Plomer 54 although the four national ornaments are wider (33 mm.) and are not separated by bars] || *LONDON*, | Printed by *Thomas Hodgkin*, for *H. Herringman, E. Brewſter,* | *T. Baſſett, R. Chiſwell, M. Wotton, G. Conyers*, M DC XCII. [with rule above date].

*Notes:* 2°. Wing J1006; *Congreve* 45.

PR2600 1692

KENNETT, BASIL.

[within double rules] *Romæ Antiquæ Notitia:* | Or, The ANTIQUITIES of | ROME. | In Two PARTS. | I. A Short HISTORY of the *Riſe, Progreſs,* and *Decay* | of the *Common-Wealth*. | II. A Deſcription of the *CITY:* An Account of the *Religion,* | *Civil Government* and *Art* of *War;* with the *Remarkable* | *Cuſtoms* and *Ceremonies, Publick* and *Private.* | With *Copper CUTS* of the *Principal Buildings,* &c. | To which are prefix'd Two ESSAYS: concerning the *Roman* | Learning, and the *Roman* Education. || By *BASIL KENNETT* of C. C. C. *Oxon.* || Dedicated to his Highneſs the Duke of *GLOCESTER.* || — *Nec deſinat unquam* | *Tecum Graia loqui, tecum Romana vetuſtas.* Claudian. || The Fifth Edition Reviſed and Corrected. || [engraving of a building at Oxford, signed on the left '*MB. ſ. U. O.*'] || *LONDON,* | Printed for T. CHILD, at the *White-Hart,* and R. KNAPLOCK, | at the *Biſhop's Head,* in St. *Paul's Church-yard,* 1713.

*Notes:* 8°. Congreve had the 1696 edition. See *Congreve* 341.

DG76 .K34 1713

MONTFAUCON DE VILLARS, ABBÉ DE.

LE COMTE | DE | GABALIS, | OU | ENTRETIENS | SUR LES SCIENCES | SECRETES. | *Quod tanto impendio abſconditur,* | *etiam ſolum-modò demonſtrare,* | *deſtruere est.* Tertull. | [orn. (18 x 29): flowers and scrollwork] | A PARIS., | Chez CLAUDE BARBIN, au Palais | ſur le Perron de la Ste Chapelle. || M. DC. LXX. | *Avec Privilege du Roy.*

*Notes:* 12°. *Congreve* 119. Congreve's own copy with his name on the title page was purchased by The University of Tennessee Library in 1938.

BF1522 .V4 1670

OSBORNE, THOMAS, DUKE OF LEEDS.

[within double rules] 𝕮𝖔𝖕𝖎𝖊𝖘 & 𝕰𝖝𝖙𝖗𝖆𝖈𝖙𝖘 | OF SOME | LETTERS | Written to and from | The Earl of *DANBY* | (now Duke of *LEEDS*) | IN THE | Years 1676, 1677, and 1678. | With particular | REMARKS | Upon ſome of them. || Publiſhed by his GRACE'S Direction. || *LONDON:* | Printed for 𝕵𝖔𝖍𝖓 𝕹𝖎𝖈𝖍𝖔𝖑𝖘𝖔𝖓 at the *Queens-Arms* | in *Little-Britain,* 1710.

*Notes:* 8°. *Congreve* 219.

DA447 .L4A2

SCARRON, PAUL.

[within double rules] THE | Whole Comical | WORKS | OF | Monſr. *SCARRON.* | CONTAINING | I. His Comical Romance of a Company of Stage- | Players. In Three Parts, Compleat. | II. All his Novels and Hiſtories. | III. His Select Letters, Characters, &c. | *A Great Part of which never before in* Engliſh. || Tranſlated by Mr.

*Tho. Brown*, Mr. *Savage,* | and Others. ‖ — — *Ridiculum acri* |
*Fortius & Melius Magnas plerumq; Secat res.* Hor. | *Rebus in Anguſtis*
*facile eſt contemnere Vitam:* | *Fortiter ille Facit, qui miſer eſſe poteſt.*
Mart. ‖ *LONDON,* | Printed for *S.* and *J. Sprint,* at the *Bell,* and
*J. Nicholſon,* | at the *King's-Arms* in *Little-Britain; R. Parker,* under
| the *Royal-Exchange,* and *Benj. Tooke,* at the *Middle-* | *Temple-Gate*
in *Fleet-Street.* MDCC.

*Notes:* 8°. Wing S829. Congreve possessed the 3rd edition (1712).
See *Congreve* 572. Purchased from Maggs Brothers, London, in 1959.

PQ1919 .A23 1700

SCUDERY, GEORGE DE.
ALARIC, | OV | ROME　　VAINCUË. | POËME　　HEROÏQUE. |
DEDIE' A LA SERENISSIME | REYNE DE SUEDE. | PAR
MONSIEVR DE SCVDERY, | GOVVERNEVR DE NOSTRE
DAME | DE LA GARDE. | [orn. (33 x 40): interwoven foliage and
flowers] | *Jouxte la Copie,* | A PARIS, | Chez AVGUSTIN COURBE',
dans la petite Salle | du Palais, à la Palme. ‖ M. DC. LV.

*Notes:* 12°. *Congreve* 32. Has the bookplate of Bridgewater Library.

PQ1921 .A7 1655

SHADWELL, THOMAS.
The DRAMATICK | WORKS | OF | *Thomas　Shadwell,* Eſq; | In
FOUR VOLUMES. ‖ ‖ *LONDON:* | Printed for J. KNAPTON, at
the *Crown* in St. | *Paul's Church-Yard;* and J. TONSON, at |
*Shakeſpear's Head* over-againſt *Katharine-Street* | in the *Strand.*
M DCC XX.

*Notes:* 12°. *Congreve* 566.

PR3671 .S8 1720

TERENCE.
[within　double　rules]　*TERENCE's* | COMEDIES: ‖ Made
*ENGLISH*. | WITH HIS | LIFE; | AND SOME | REMARKS at the
End. ‖ By Several HANDS. ‖ *LONDON:* | Printed for *A. Swall* and
*T. Childe,* at the | *Unicorn,* at the Weſt-End of St. *Paul's* |
Church-yard. 1694.

*Notes:* 8°. Wing T749; *Congreve* 595. Congreve's own copy, with his
signature partly obliterated. The title page is reproduced in *Congreve,*
facing p. 100. The translation is attributed to Laurence Echard by
Stonehill.

PA6756 .A1E5 1694

VILLIERS, GEORGE, DUKE OF BUCKINGHAM.

THE | REHEARSAL, | As it is novv Acted | AT THE | Theatre-Royal. ‖ The Fifth Edition with Amendments and | large Additions by the AUTHOR. ‖ *LONDON,* | Printed for *Thomas Dring,* and ſold by *John* | *Newton* under the *King's Head* Tavern | over againſt the *Inner-Temple-Gate* | in *Fleet-Street.* 1687.

*Notes:* 4°. Wing B5327; Macdonald 165e. *Congreve* 406c. Purchased from Maggs Brothers, London, 1959.

PR3328 .B5A7 1687

See also 121. and 122. in the Congreve catalog.

# INDEX OF AUTHORS AND TITLES
# LISTED IN THE CATALOG